SECRETS

OF THE

MOON

D1598511

Myth and Mysticism,
History and Science

Andrew Osiow

ISBN: 979-8-9871842-3-3 (Paperback)

ISBN: 979-8-98718424-0 (Ebook)

Library of Congress Control Number: 2023900192

Many friends and family supported this endeavor, but I offer a special thanks to three women who helped launch my journey. Jenna Kind, Gillian Mantchev, and especially Michelle Valdovinos.

I also want to acknowledge the many great editors who contributed to this project: Graham Southorn, Tatiana Wilde, John Knight, John Byram and Barbara Noe Kennedy. Thanks also to Marissa DeCuir of Books Forward for publicity, Hannah Robertson of Books Fluent for her comprehensive management, and Hannah Gaskamp for layout and design. Finally, I add a special thanks to Roberta Morris of Leave It to 'Berta for her original design and amazing cover.

Contents

Part 2: Spring—The Moon and Life

Part 3: Summer—Believing in the Moon

Part 4: Autumn—The Moon and Us

Part 5: Another Winter—Returning to the Moon

Preface

My path to the Moon was a random act of discovery with a twist. The idea first came to me while attending a lecture by Dr. Neil deGrasse Tyson. Humorous irony is a well-known trademark of Dr. Tyson, but the Moon was not his target that evening. He chose instead to regale the audience with a personal account of Pluto's infamous planetary demotion and the unexpected public outcry.

While Dr. Tyson seemed bemused that something so trivial could cause such a dramatic response, I wondered if the opposite could be true. Was there another object, perhaps astronomical, that had real world significance, but trivialized? The Moon came to mind as a likely candidate. Pluto was far away and a 20th century discovery, while the Moon was close to Earth and had been known since prehistoric times. It seemed like an overly easy comparison, but it made me question the depth of my Moon knowledge. I would have to check it out.

That my inspiration for this book came during a scientific lecture says something about me. I am a fan and happily inhale any morsel of pop science nourishment that comes my way. My fond childhood memories of the Apollo missions have interested me all my life. Without giving it much thought at the time, I believed my Moon IQ was comfortably high. Addressing my concern would only take a modest amount of research time, but I was curious to see if my little flip of logic was a bit of serendipity in disguise.

It turns out my suspicions about the Moon were true, but even more so than I thought. Its presence in our lives extends far beyond what is commonly understood. It retains a mystical enchantment, but common Moon knowledge has become less common as our civilization has grown. This seemed both strange and tragic. As science reveals more about the

Moon, we seem less aware of our older bonds. I also discovered to my dismay that I was part of this trend. As a supposed Moon expert, I hardly rated better than most.

My eventual take away from Dr. Tyson's lecture was a refresher in the irony of human perception. Pluto's fall from planetary stardom had been purely scientific. Starting in 1992, astronomers began uncovering similar sized objects at the far reaches of the solar system. Pluto could not remain a planet in the traditional sense alongside a sea of the trans-Neptunian objects. If it did, hundreds of them would need to be reclassified as well.

Dr. Tyson accidentally joined Pluto's swan song by simply doing his job. When the famed Hayden Planetarium reopened in 2000 under his direction, it included an updated display of the solar system without Pluto. The change reflected the future of astronomy, but the New York Times pointed out the glaring omission. When Pluto officially was demoted in 2006, Dr. Tyson was inundated with impassioned pleas to reverse the decision.

Pluto had unexpectedly transcended the world of astronomy to gain a soft spot in American culture. For many people with only a rudimentary knowledge of astronomy, Pluto was a childhood memory from third-grade science that shared its name with a Disney cartoon character. It was just unthinkable for Pluto to be anything less than a planet. This sentiment has yet to diminish as I often get a similar response whenever I retell the story.

The Moon is more of a forgotten childhood friend than Pluto ever was, or maybe we have never got properly introduced to it in the first place. Its connection to our lives runs so deep that telling the Moon's unknown story is like revealing a hidden part of humanity. I decided it was a tale worth sharing because there was something to learn from the overlooked Moon. One of life's biggest lessons is that we often fail to see things for what they really are. If that is true, then perhaps the Moon has a lot to teach us.

The Second Preface

The Moon is not necessarily a sensitive subject, but it touches many areas that are. What we believe is often more important than what we know. We are more likely swayed by our personal experiences than science facts. I believe you will have little success in changing a person's mind by telling them they are wrong, and that is not my intent. I simply suggest keeping an open mind as I reveal a Moon you might not know. Science often is seen as a weapon against non-scientific concepts, but the joy of discovery comes from our invention of science and accepting it. It is the key to unlocking a beautiful Moon.

As Copernicus labored on his book *On the Revolutions of the Heavenly Spheres*, he faced a similar dilemma, but with dire consequences. He had clearly stated that Earth revolved around the Sun, and this unconventional idea was almost certain to cause friction with an authoritarian Catholic Church. This is possibly the reason he repeatedly delayed publishing, and the final printed version did not appear until after his death.

To soften the blow, the publisher added a second preface. It stated that Copernicus merely used the model of Earth orbiting the Sun as means to simplify the calculations of planetary motion. It wasn't meant to be taken as a literal truth. Even though it was controversially added without consent from Copernicus, there was truth. The bulk of the book dealt with an improved system for calculating planetary motion. To paraphrase, it was a better way to understand the physical universe without challenging one's theological beliefs.

It is unclear if the preface made any difference. The book was technically challenging for its time, and its world-changing idea was buried deep among a dense array of tables and calculations. Initial concern over a negative response turned out to be unwarranted. The book started out as a poor seller, attracting a small audience with no controversy. The Church considered it inappropriate some 70 years later when other astronomers began to side publicly with Copernicus.

This second preface is not intended to protect the book from adversarial readers but to remind them that science allows for a unique form of objectivity. It has become the big revealer of our world, and an integral part of our society. It is a repeated theme in this book. Science shows us a reality that is nonnegotiable but not necessarily incompatible with all our beliefs. Despite a tendency to be leveraged heavily in a culture war, science is only interested with the provable aspects of nature.

One overlooked conclusion to the Copernican Revolution is the lasting impact it had on organized religion. Except for gaining the reputation of being a bully of science in the renaissance age, the Catholic Church has continued mostly unchanged. The real outcome of the Copernican Revolution was an improved way of looking at the night sky which the Church eventually embraced. It was precisely what the second preface had originally suggested. The Church eventually removed Copernicus' work from its restricted list, and it became viewed as complementary teachings. The result was not only a shift in what people understood but also in what they believed.

Introduction: The Moon's Shadow

A solar eclipse is the Moon's best trick to getting some well-deserved attention. When one is close at hand, the Moon predictably trends high on the Internet as an experience-hungry society rummages for optimal viewing details. We quickly consume the obligatory celestial diagrams that remind us how a solar eclipse works, and a few of us might invest a little more time to catch up on any science-related news. The Moon makes a comeback from near obscurity to regain a former glory like an old rock band returning for a farewell tour. Die-hard eclipse fans will scout around for the "best seats in the house" to find the epic sweet spot known as totality, but most of us will settle for the easily accessible mass viewing area of a partial solar eclipse. In either case, we pause in unison to witness the awesome promise of darkness in the middle of the day.

During the precious few minutes of totality, the world we know disappears, and we enter the Moon's domain. Its massive shadow silently races toward us at supersonic speeds and finally swings overhead. We marvel equally like giddy children at the elegantly simple spectacle before us. We miraculously stare at the once dazzling Sun without the usual health concerns. The air noticeably chills, and a few bright stars appear in the dusk-like sky. All around us, the horizon returns to the early dawn no matter where we look. The feeling is an unearthly mixture of spiritual enlightenment and scientific awakening. We have traveled back in time to see the Moon of our prehistoric ancestors without the fear that came from their lack of understanding. We see the world in an altered state, but our euphoria is short-lived. Within minutes, Earth's spin throws us out of the Moon's shadow, and we return to our regular terrestrial-bound lives. Our onetime lunar connection becomes a cherished memory, but our newly found interest in the Moon typically fades away along with its shadow.

We live in an odd time of indifference for the Moon. Our brilliant achievement of walking on the Moon has unexpectedly made it passé. The Apollo missions are now summed up with a quaint nod to the past and share equal time with the social trends, politics, and free love of the sixties. Today, we use our phones to explore the Moon. Ironically, the information age is a direct continuation of the space age, and that same technology gives us the ability to reevaluate anything we choose on a whim, including the Moon. Against our sophisticated notion of space travel shaped by years of visually polished science fiction, the Moon is losing the significance it once held in our lives. Its magical glow from childhood is lost, and the same might be said of our civilization as we move into the 21st century. As we search for value in the newness of technology, there will never be a Moon 2.0.

Perhaps the closest we can get to reinventing the Moon is by going back, and the Artemis missions give us a second chance. Named after the Roman Moon goddess and twin sister of Apollo, the historic symbolism is clear. With goals both social and scientific, it's a declaration of how far we have come and how far we have yet to go. The Moon of our future is the Moon of our past, but spaceflight is just one thread of many that tie us to the Moon. The Moon of our past is also the Moon of our far distant past, and we have discovered many lunar connections before, during, and since the Apollo landings. Most of them are less dramatic than walking on the Moon, but they are so numerous that our overall unfamiliarity becomes unfathomable.

Like the classic Twilight Zone preamble from the same sixties era, the Moon lies on the boundary between the pit of our fears and summit of our knowledge and acts as a bridge between those two worlds. It is both a tool of civilization and a cultural icon repeatedly seen in mythology and literature. It is the first astronomical object to be drawn and studied, and the first alien world to be visited both in fiction and in real life. Its many connections are strewn all around us, but the Moon's least known link to our lives is also its most intriguing. Lifeless though it may be, the Moon is a critical component of our ecosystem. Without it, life on Earth would be very different and perhaps not even possible.

The book is designed to help you become your own astronaut by taking an imaginary journey to the Moon and back over the course of a year. Every two to three years we get 13 full moons in a single year, and the book mimics that fact with 13 chapters. The chapters are further organized into threes, like months in a season, with each addressing a larger theme. We begin in winter by looking at the Moon's story and how it matured from an element of fiction into an object of discovery, and how that transformation revealed an unexpected new beginning. Spring covers the overlooked ways that the Moon impacts our daily lives. Summer shows us a Moon where science and unscientific ideas meet. Autumn concludes with the Moon's uniqueness and what it says about us. The last chapter returns us to the Moon for wisdom as some of its earliest messages.

As you read through each chapter, you'll explore two major narratives of discovery: how crucial the Moon is for our survival, and how it became a multifaceted cornerstone of our society. The Moon's importance in our lives is inspired by fulfilling both roles, but the Moon's unexpected rarity makes for an awe-inspiring conclusion. If the Moon is a result of a once-in-a-trillion cosmic event, then it also defines how rare and special we are. This is the ultimate message from the Moon. We can all share in being part of something bigger. If we are all special, then we are all worth helping, all worth saving.

PART 1:

WINTER
The Moon: Facts and Fiction

The Moon dances between worlds of fact and fiction. There are few things that are so well understood and yet can still willingly mystify us. Our shared view of the Moon often is based more on fiction than fact, but science has added a new story that is just as intriguing as a fictional tale.

December: Dark Side of the Moon
January: Newton's Moon
February: A Piece of the Moon

Moon Secret 1: The Moon wobbles.

The Moon's motion is more complex than we can easily see. Although one side is visible to us, the Moon wobbles every month, which allows us to see up to 59 percent of its surface. These extra motions, technically known as the Moon's libration, are difficult to notice with a casual glance but have been known to astronomers for centuries, with the earliest maps of libration zones dating back to 1645. Today, with the benefit of time-lapse photography, we can clearly see the Moon for what it is, a wobbling sphere rolling in space.

The Moon

But all of the things that belong to the day
Cuddle to sleep to be out of her way
And flowers and children close their eyes
Till up in the morning the sun shall arise.

ROBERT LOUIS STEVENSON

DECEMBER:
The Dark Side of the Moon

The Cold Moon (American Indian)

(Science gives us an untarnished view of the unknown)

Journey to the Other Side

The Moon is the single most viewed object in history, and yet most of us are unaware of that fact. All of Earth's most viewed destinations pale in comparison when considering the thousands of generations that have unwittingly shared the same experience. This universal accessibility might make watching the Moon seem routine, but it makes for a powerful thought. The Moon connects us to the rest of the world and the past. From Newton to Jules Verne, virtually anyone you know, either personally or historically, has seen the Moon and pondered its meaning. It is one single Moon for all humankind.

Thanks to the space race of the 1960s, we now see the Moon as a destination conquered. It is likely the first thing that most people will say about the Moon. Like other inaccessible locations, we champion the fact that someone has been there. Originally, 12 humans walked on the Moon and another 12 made that long journey of nearly a quarter of a million miles. Together they formed one of the most exclusive clubs on Earth. For over 50 years, they were the only humans to have seen the Moon up close. Others eventually will follow, but no one has returned to the Moon in over half a lifetime. As the decades have rolled on, the Moon landings have slowly become a distant secondhand experience.

Some argue that we should have included poets or philosophers alongside the bold astronauts as they might have found better words to capture the moment. This seems unfair as we have never asked the same from other explorers, and perhaps it was for the best. Live video transmissions were a fairly new technology. Astronauts with little public speaking experience made unrehearsed performances while the Moon took center stage. Whether it was from lunar orbit or on the surface of the Moon, we saw what the astronauts saw and were left to work out our own meaning. Live videos with added personal commentary are the norm of today's online community. Our modern view of ourselves began with our first closeup of the Moon.

The first Moon visitors were the crew of Apollo 8. Arriving at the Moon on Christmas Eve 1968, they had traveled far, like the three wise men of the Nativity. Although this mission was later eclipsed by the fame of Apollo 11, its goal is often still considered the most daring stage of the Apollo program. The crew would escape the relative safety of low Earth orbit to become the first humans to orbit the Moon. This meant they would also be the first to travel through the infamous dark side of the Moon. Known as such because no direct radio contact was possible, Apollo 8 would be completely cut off from the rest of the world. It was during this critical phase that the spacecraft was required to perform a perfect course correction to enter lunar orbit. The crew would be totally alone. There would be no help from mission control should something go wrong.

As Apollo 8 was about to enter radio silence, astronaut Jim Lovell calmly uttered the optimistic but ominous phrase,

"We'll see you on the other side."

He would later say that waiting for the engine to complete its firing was "the longest four minutes he ever spent." Mission control could do little more than wait, but after nearly 36 minutes, Apollo 8 emerged from the other side exactly as expected. Executed flawlessly with the aid of the capsule's onboard computer, the course correction had gone without incident. Humanity had triumphed over the unknown with a little help from technology.

Although this was the first time the dark side of the Moon had been seen in person, it was not entirely unknown. Both Soviet and American unmanned probes had surveyed it years before making it the second world in the solar system to be completely mapped. The first pictures of the far side had been taken by the Soviet probe Luna 3 in 1959. By 1967, both countries had produced detailed maps of nearly the entire Moon. Lunar Orbiter 1, the first probe of the American survey series, is famous for taking the first picture of Earth from space in 1966. A much clearer color picture of earthrise taken by the crew of Apollo 8 would gain international acclaim two years later.

Apollo 8 is often viewed as just a preliminary step for Apollo 11, but its true significance lies in the new perspective it gave people back on Earth. Shortly after their emergence from the dark side, the crew made their first television broadcast, which featured angling the TV camera toward the Moon's surface and pointing out recognizable features. For the first time in history, the people of Earth saw a Moon unadorned by their imagination. It was an opportunity for subjective beliefs to be reevaluated.

All the Moon images taken by Apollo 8 and other missions since can now easily be found online. We can repeat the journey to the Moon virtually, without even taking a step. Any conceivable fact about the Moon is at our fingertips, but raw data is only part of the Internet. It has evolved into an interconnected journal of human experience and opinion. When we search for the Moon online, we go beyond science and folklore, and step into the visual interpretations of others. The Internet supplies an endless array, but two videos are notable for using similar AI technology to produce opposite results.

The first video is a stunning restoration of the Moon's surface from a camera mounted on the lunar rover of Apollo 16. The other is a disturbingly realistic glimpse of a Deep Fake called *In Event of Moon Disaster*. While the enhanced footage from Apollo 16 gives the Moon a new sense of realism, the fake introduces President Nixon delivering a fictional eulogy for the astronauts of Apollo 11.

Today, we exist in a future that Apollo scientists could not have foreseen. The vision of Artificial Intelligence has often been portrayed as villainous machines intent on destroying our civilization. The threat of our technology now plays out for real as we ironically must choose what to do with it. Are we doomed to build a new Dark Age within the midst of our technological brilliance? Or can we find ways to navigate safely through our darker nature? The story of the Moon and Apollo 8 might offer us hope in this dilemma. Once we got there, the darker side of the unknown became a place for new reflection. Self-awareness is always our best means of illumination.

On most nights, the Moon hangs in the night sky, waiting to be observed by anyone and everyone. Far away from a fast-paced digital world, it invites us to reach a more tranquil state of mind. Its bright side has enlightened us for thousands of years, but perhaps its greatest gift in our current age is a sense of unity. When people from all walks of life are invited to view the Moon through a telescope, they invariably experience the same unclouded euphoria. While the Internet may tempt us with a false sense of authority, the Moon can inspire a sense of common humility.

When Apollo 8 visited the Moon, it became a real and somewhat ordinary place. Jim Lovell described it as looking like "Plaster of Paris" or grayish beach sand. This trivial assessment is important to remember. Our tinted romance with the Moon holds us back from seeing something more amazing. Apollo 8 astronaut William Anders, who became famous for taking the earthrise photograph, might have caught the moment best:

> "We came all this way to explore the Moon, and the most important thing is that we discovered the Earth."

Going to the Moon gave us a new perspective of Earth and ourselves. Anders likened Earth to a single glass Christmas tree ornament alone in a completely dark room, something to cherish and respect. By looking back from the Moon, Apollo 8 offered the world a chance to look at itself, but that potential has been there all along. One small look at the Moon can fill us with a sense of wonder, but one long glance back at Earth from the Moon may remind us of who we are.

Looking at the Bright Side

The "dark side of the Moon" inspires a sense of poetic mystery. The "bright side of the Moon" is not so compelling, but it might best represent a region of our minds where experience is built on fact. Like the Moon, these two halves of our perception can coexist. The scientific side of the Moon is nothing new as it was one of the earliest subjects of scientific study.

Our first real empirical knowledge about the Moon comes from the Babylonians. They were first to notice that solar eclipses come in cycles, a system that's still in use today. They also measured changes in the Moon's size as it regularly moved closer and farther away from Earth. The Greeks would later establish a connection between the Moon and the tides, and correctly deduced that a lunar eclipse was caused by the Moon passing through Earth's shadow. While short on new insight, medieval astronomy provided an excellent record of major events in the night sky. The English monk Bede the Venerable wrote extensively on the Moon's seasonal motion in 725. This included its tidal influence, but a matching scientific explanation would have to wait until the enlightenment of Newtonian physics.

Our current scientific understanding of the Moon goes well beyond the limits of the casual observer, but it can still be broken down into a few basic concepts. The shaded pattern of the Moon's surface results from its volcanic past. The darker areas were once impact craters that filled with seas of iron rich liquid magma. Beyond lunar volcanism, there are two scientific principles behind our view of the Moon. Ambient illumination explains why the Moon appears to shine, and tidal lock explains why we only see one side. These two concepts also represent two distinct levels of thinking, with one being more intuitive than the other.

When the Moon appears dark during a new moon, we often still see its silhouette. This is due to earthshine, which is a less common example of ambient illumination. Similar to moonlight, light is first reflected from Earth before being bounced back from the Moon. While we can trace the idea of moonlight back to ancient Greece, Leonardo da Vinci was the first person to describe earthshine. Like many other artists, he was aware of bouncing light on Earth and correctly concluded that it would also bounce between objects in space. Because the light is traveling farther, earthshine often is too faint to see easily. The best chance to view it is during a new or crescent moon in the springtime when Earth's atmosphere is reflecting the largest amount of light back into space.

The one-sided Moon is the best example of an effect seen throughout the solar system. If a moon stays in a close stable orbit around a planet for long enough, the gravity or tidal force from that planet will regulate the moon's rotational speed until it is synced to orbit around the planet. If we could look up from Mars at either of its two moons, we would always see the same side, because they are tidal locked to Mars, and there are pictures taken by the Martian rover Curiosity to prove it. Some of Jupiter's moons orbit close enough to directly affect each other so the tidal effect on them is more complex, but the general principle is the same.

Tidal lock is a mathematical and physical abstraction. One simplified way to think about it is to consider the Moon as two halves. At any point in time, half the Moon is spinning away from Earth while the other half is spinning toward it. Earth's gravity pulls equally on both halves of the Moon, attempting to slow down one side while speeding up the other. As a result, the Moon's spin slowly is adjusted until it appears not to spin at all.

We naturally compare the Moon to other real-world experiences on Earth to make sense of it, but many aspects of the Moon's nature have no equivalence on Earth. Often, the farther an idea is from everyday experience, the easier it is to be misunderstood. This has often led to conspiracies inspired by photographs taken during our landing on the

Moon. Learning about the Moon, or the world, requires trusting in the science that explains it. We do this all the time with other parts of our daily lives. No one ever questions the science behind the Internet, and yet very few of us can truly say how it really works. The Moon represents many other elements of our psyche that can easily cloud our judgement, but the Moon also offers a lesson in how we can view the science that describes it.

A Moon Story

The Moon's story is an ancient tale that stretches far back to our earliest imaginations. Its fictional side remains a dominant force in our culture, but the Moon's story is also a chronology of our science. As our understanding of the universe progressed, so did our view of the Moon. The earliest views of the Moon are sketchy. Many details have been lost over time, but its prominent place in the night sky would have guaranteed it an equally prominent role in the fiction of preliterate societies. Some examples of the oldest surviving Moon tales come through oral traditions of cultures that predate written language.

For the Inuit, the Moon was Anningan, brother of the Sun goddess Malina, whom he constantly chased in a jealous rage. For the Australian Aboriginal peoples, the roles were reversed. The Moon was Bahloo and was chased in vain by his would-be lover, the Sun goddess Yhi. To the Cahuilla tribes of Southwest America, the Moon was Menily, a beautiful maiden who taught the people arts and crafts before being chased back to the sky. Along the West African coast, the Fon people of southern Benin called the Moon Gleti, and she was the mother of the stars and wife to the Sun.

The earliest Moon god in recorded history was called Nanna (Sin) by the Sumer people who lived in Mesopotamia around 3000 B.C. Nanna was depicted as a bull with horns clearly inspired by the crescent moon. The oldest known poetry also comes from this time. It is a love poem recited by the head Moon priestess in a fertility ritual meant to ensure ongoing prosperity. Later civilizations would continue to associate the Moon with a female persona and strengthen the gender connection. In China it was Chiang. For the Greeks, it was Phoebe, Selene, Artemis, and Hecate. And for the Romans, it was Luna and Diana.

The last famous personification of the Moon occurred in the Middle Ages. By that time, classic myths had given way to heroic tales containing a moral message. The pattern of a human face seen in the Moon was interpreted as the remains of a man who was guilty of theft and imprisoned for eternity. His sad tale is found in the medieval poem *Mon in the Moone* (known today as the *Man in the Moon*), and it represents a critical change in how we saw the Moon. Even in fiction, the Moon was becoming a place. Coincidentally, the Moon completed this transition in fiction with the similarly titled *The Man in the Moone* written by Francis Godwin in 1632.

Godwin's tale features a Spaniard called Domingo Gonsales who escapes pirates by flying to the Moon with the use of powerful wild swans. Although this was not the first literary mention of traveling to the Moon, its success triggered a cascade of further developments. The book remained popular for a long time and inspired authors for centuries, including Edgar Allan Poe and Jules Verne. Cyrano de Bergerac parodied the work in 1657 where Cyrano as the author finds Gonsales still on the Moon. The book was also the basis for the highly successful play called *Emperor of the Moon*. Written in 1687, it would become the best-known work of Aphra Behn, one of the earliest female playwrights.

Two of the earliest stories that feature the Moon as a place are *The Dream* by astronomer Johannes Kepler and *The Tale of the Bamboo Cutter* from ninth- or tenth-century Japanese literature. In *The Dream*, Kepler recalls a fictional dream where a boy and his witch mother travel to the Moon with the aid of a daemon, or good spirit. *The Tale of the Bamboo Cutter* is the story of a baby girl found in the woods by the titular character who raises her to become a beautiful and mysterious princess. Admired by all, she eventually reveals that she is from a kingdom on the Moon to which she must return.

These stories, along with a political satire called *A True History*, written by Lucian in the second century A.D., often are cited as early forms of science fiction for using themes such as space travel and alien civilizations. While Goodwin and Kepler were clearly inspired by the science of the Copernican Revolution, the reasoning behind the others is not so obvious. One explanation might come from an ancient myth that birds migrated to the Moon during winter. Travel to far distant lands was also becoming more common, and the Moon's light and dark patterns could have been interpreted as the continents and oceans of another world.

Modern science fiction arrived with the Industrial Age. Technology replaced magic, and its tantalizing power was captured in fantastic adventures that might one day be possible. Visiting the Moon was a natural topic, so the Moon changed to become an achievable destination in the near future. *A Voyage to the Moon* published by George Tucker in 1827 was one of the first. Edgar Allan Poe followed in 1835 with *The Unparalleled Adventure of One Hans Pfaall,* and this era was capped off with Jules Verne's definitive *From the Earth to the Moon* in the early 1860s.

Verne's work foretells three men traveling to the Moon using an incredibly powerful gun called the Columbiad. Like *The Man in the Moone,* it would also inspire others for generations. French film pioneer Georges Méliès followed with the equally inspiring film adaptation of *A Trip to the Moon* in 1902. *From the Earth to the Moon* also would serve as an inspiration for rocket pioneers throughout the 20th century. The reality of Apollo 11 mirrored many elements of the story including a Florida launch site and a Pacific Ocean splashdown. Even the space capsule would be similar in size and shape to the one described by Jules Verne and was deservedly named Columbia in his honor.

It is during the era of early space exploration that the Moon made its final transition in literature to that of an inhabited world as either a permanent base or human colony. Many early examples are found in the works of H. G. Wells, Issacs Asimov, Arthur C. Clarke, and particularly Robert A. Heinlein. The Moon becomes a background for any kind of human activity. In Heinlein's Hugo-Award-winning novel *The Moon is a Harsh Mistress,* the Moon has become a penal colony that harkens back to the old fable of a man trapped in the Moon. From a multi-faced goddess to a second home, the Moon's long metamorphosis appropriately concluded with humanity's journey to the Moon.

Seeing in the Dark

I f you had to write a novel that captured the history of humanity's interplay with the Moon, the Apollo Moon landings would make a natural conclusion. But such a novel would end with an unexpected twist—one that turned Apollo into a new myth. Moon landing conspiracies are nearly as old as the Moon missions they hope to defame, and they doggedly have remained entrenched in our collective view of the Moon despite the best efforts of scientists and historians to prove them wrong.

The earliest Moon conspiracy began in 1976 with a self-published work by Bill Kaysing. Hired by the NASA subcontractor Rocketdyne as a technical writer in 1956, Kaysing leveraged his previous position to tell an insider's story. He had in fact left Rocketdyne in 1962 for unknown reasons. At the time of his departure, the company still was struggling with engineering challenges of the Saturn V's F-1 engine. Kaysing later would assert the failures were unsurmountable, and that NASA deliberately covered it up and secretly used the less powerful B-1 engines instead. The launch supposedly would look the same, but only have enough thrust to get the rocket into a low Earth orbit. These claims eventually would be disproved in 2013 by Bezos Expeditions when it recovered one of the five F-1 engines used by Apollo 11 from 14,000 feet under the Atlantic Ocean.

Conspiracy theories flourished in the 1970s, and NASA was an easy target. It had achieved what many considered impossible, and the Moon was too far away to visually verify the landings. With the Kennedy assassination and Nixon's Watergate, scandals had already scarred the public with a sense of distrust. Investigative-style reporting grew to fill the void of authority. Even the word "conspiracy" evolved to mean a plot to subvert the truth. The burgeoning conspiracy culture went mainstream in 1978 with the release of *Capricorn One*, a sci-fi thriller about a faked Mars mission intentionally made to look like Apollo. With the birth of the Internet, Moon conspiracies found a new home.

Alternate "truths" about the Apollo missions are sadly easy to find. Either NASA never went to the Moon or is concealing evidence of alien life on the Moon. It doesn't matter that these two stories contradict one another. They've even been combined to suggest that NASA created the original conspiracy simply to hide the evidence of alien life on the Moon. The film *2001: A Space Odyssey* might have been the inspiration for this version as a government hoax on the Moon is used as a subplot. Its strikingly realistic visuals are the source of yet another conspiracy theory suggesting that NASA needed extra time to develop its new rocket technology and faked the first two Apollo missions with the help of director Stanley Kubrick.

In 2009, NASA produced additional evidence to counter conspiracy arguments. Forty-two years after its original Lunar Orbiter series ended, NASA returned to the Moon with the technically superior Lunar Reconnaissance Orbiter probe. While not solely intended to debunk conspiracy theories, the LRO still would champion the cause by taking high-resolution images of the entire Moon down to a half-meter resolution. Within a year, a new detailed map of the Moon was released to the public, which included all the Apollo landing sites. Pictures from the LRO clearly revealed tracks on the Moon's surface left behind by the astronauts. The only sign of life on the Moon's desolate surface was our own.

The LRO should have logically ended the era of NASA conspiracies, but conspiracy theories are not about proving a rational point. They are an aberration of a mental process called illusory pattern perception. Our brains have a natural skill to find patterns everywhere, but lacking evidence we err on the side of a possible match. "Better safe than sorry," as the saying goes, as in, there is more to be lost from missing a pattern than seeing one that isn't there. This behavior has long been suspected as the root of conspiracy beliefs, and now there is some proof. Reported in the *European Journal of Social Psychology* in 2017, researchers made a correlation with irrational beliefs and compulsive pattern matching. People who saw patterns in random coin tosses were more likely to accept a conspiracy theory as true.

Conspiracies, Moon landing or otherwise, are not likely to disappear soon. The Moon has unexpectedly transformed into a central character in the drama of life with a backstory that extends beyond our earliest legends. It is a tale as grand as any yet written, but it competes for our attention among a constant stream of false leads. For some they are the tent poles of a fictional world that empowers them to remain steadfast to a belief about themselves, but they can also serve a useful purpose for the rest of us. Understanding the mechanics of a conspiracy theory can give us insight into shared human frailties. Moon conspiracies, for example, can teach us how to spot the source of a self-destructive effect.

How can we determine fact from fallacy, the bright from the dark? The same researchers that study conspiracy theories suggest critical thinking as a basic solution. Begin by trusting the science that created the world. Everything we have learned about the Moon is waiting to be rediscovered online. Actively searching for factual stories on the Moon is a first step to finding truths about the rest of the world. Isaac Newton is famous for saying,

"If I have seen further, it is by standing on the shoulders of giants."

Thanks to the science behind technology, we can all truly say the same whether or not we realize it.

Moon Secret 2: The Moon is a giant lemon.

The Moon only looks round from our point of view. It is slightly oval shaped, which some astronomers have dubbed lemon like. The technical term is an oblate spheroid or flattened sphere. Its oval profile is very slight and can't be seen from Earth because it faces in our direction. The shape is a result of Earth's gravity shaping the Moon when it had a molten core. Earth pulled at the Moon's magma until it formed slight bulges that faced directly toward and away from Earth. After 200 million years, the Moon cooled enough to make the lemon shape permanent.

Above the Dock
Above the quiet dock in mid night,
Tangled in the tall mast's corded height,
Hangs the moon. What seemed so far away
Is but a child's balloon, forgotten after play.
T. E. HULME

JANUARY:
Newton's Moon

The Quiet Moon (Celtic)

(Awe and wonder are now a measured reality)

Heavenly Spheres

The Moon is an actual place. While obvious, this statement symbolizes a level of underappreciated scientific sophistication that we all possess. The Moon's physical properties are the groundwork for understanding the rest of the universe. We know the Moon's distance from Earth, its diameter, how fast it travels through space, and even its mass. We accept these values and many others without question because we trust in the science that produced them. Our extended reality is determined by physics and mathematics.

The physical certainty of the Moon was not always so clear. It once belonged in the domain of theology and mysticism, but during the mid-16th century, the sphere of our understanding grew beyond Earth to encompass the Moon, and the rest of the night sky would follow. This transformative period is usually referred to as the Copernican Revolution, but it is neither fair nor accurate to attribute it to Nicolaus Copernicus alone. Many contributed to revealing how the solar system worked with Isaac Newton providing the final and biggest piece of the puzzle. Calling it the "Newtonian Revolution" might be more appropriate. His rules of gravity and motion became the building blocks of modern physics. Without these rules, ideas about the night sky would remain speculative. As Newton pondered gravity, the Moon was a perfect example of that force in action. The effects of Earth's pull could be observed against the Moon's orbital path. Newton gave us the undeniable reality of gravity, and the Moon helped Newton accomplish that goal.

The classic but incorrect view of an Earth-centered solar system had an incredibly long track record because it seemed perfectly reasonable and was difficult to disprove. Earth felt solid, heavy, and unmovable. The

Moon, planets, and stars revolved around Earth on giant celestial spheres made of quintessence, a fifth and perfect element. Even though this was the accepted view of how the solar system worked, there was no proof it was true. The best evidence against it was an unusually backward looping pattern of the planets known as retrograde motion. The Greek astronomer Ptolemy, who almost single-handedly institutionalized Aristotle's views on astronomy, resolved the problem with the use of epicycles. He suggested the planets were instead glued to smaller spheres that rotated within the main celestial spheres. This lopsided motion matched the astronomical data close enough to be an adequate explanation, but epicycles were a means to an end. Their existence was never questioned nor why the Moon didn't need them.

It is likely that Copernicus did not plan to reverse a thousand years of astronomical teachings. His concerns were more practical. The usual way to determine the position of the Sun, Moon, and planets was to consult the Alfonsine tables. Based on the work of Ptolemy, they were difficult to generate, and Copernicus discovered he could simplify the process if he used a model where the planets orbited the Sun. Because this would challenge the Catholic Church, which subscribed to Aristotle's view, Copernicus delayed publishing his technique in a book. He only relented after receiving encouraging feedback from colleagues. *On the Revolutions of the Heavenly Spheres*, the book that would make him a household name in science, wouldn't be printed until after his death.

Although his assumption was correct, the model that Copernicus presented had some problems that hindered broad acceptance. Resistance did not initially come from the Church, as is often portrayed. Copernicus' work was difficult to understand, and only those with a strong mathematical background could follow along. Copernicus also continued the use of the transparent celestial spheres first devised by Ptolemy. The Sun and Earth had only traded places. Copernicus' model employed perfectly circular orbits, which did not match the data. This forced Copernicus to retain Ptolemy's epicycles, which was a backward step.

Danish astronomer Tycho Brahe rejected the Copernican model. He argued that if it were true, there would be observable evidence in the form of stellar parallax—the shift in position of stars when seen from different vantage points. Specifically, Brahe was talking about a diurnal stellar parallax, which is a shift in position of stars measured from opposite sides of Earth's orbit. Such minute changes existed but were beyond the ability of Brahe to measure. The first successful measurements of stellar parallax didn't happen until 1838.

Even though his assertion about stellar parallax was incorrect, Tycho Brahe's opinion was not to be taken lightly. He had a well-established reputation for collecting the most precise astronomy data, and he was not opposed to a revolutionary idea. Like Copernicus, he accepted that the ancient views of the solar system were flawed and outdated. Instead, he proposed an unusual hybrid solution, where the other planets revolved around the Sun, but the Sun still revolved around Earth. This produced a delay in the advancement of the Copernican model. Copernicus' concerns about repercussions did not initially happen, but the Copernican Revolution was stalled.

A Tale of Two Books

Aristarchus of Samos is not as well-known as he should be. He perfectly represents that part of ancient Greek culture that is potentially amazing but tragically lost forever. We know he was a formidable astronomer who lived in the third century B.C., but details of his work are scarce. His genius is based solely on the two books we know he wrote, and we do not even know their titles. Unfortunately, only one has survived through an incomplete copy. The other we only know about by way of a brief criticism in a rival work.

The one remaining work of Aristarchus is an ingenious technique used to calculate the distance to the Sun and the Moon. Just the idea of measuring the size of the solar system demonstrates that Aristarchus was working on a higher level than many of his contemporaries. This was not mere philosophical conjecture, but an application of mathematics to produce a measurable result. Based on the geometry of the time, he reasoned you could calculate the distance to the Moon by comparing its size to the shadow of Earth during a lunar eclipse. The idea was so irrefutable that astronomers continued to use it for centuries. By Newton's time, the Moon was thought to be approximately 60 diameters away from Earth, which was quite close to the actual distance.

Calculating the distance to the Moon was not the most astounding feat Aristarchus could claim. Eighteen hundred years before Copernicus, he proposed the same revolutionary idea that Earth orbited the Sun. How Aristarchus came to this conclusion is unknown. He knew the Sun had to be farther away than the Moon and therefore bigger. Since the Sun was bigger, Aristarchus might have concluded that Earth revolved around it. It might have also been an extension to his belief that the

Sun was a star and therefore did not move. This equally advanced idea had come from his mentor Anaxagoras, one of the first to suggest that moonlight was actually bounced sunlight. We will never know the reasoning behind Aristarchus' astounding hypothesis. It has only survived because of a slightly unflattering reference in a book by the more respected Archimedes.

> "You are now aware . . . that the "universe" is the name given by most astronomers to the sphere, the centre of which is the centre of the earth, . . . But Aristarchus has brought out a book consisting of certain hypotheses . . . His hypotheses are that the fixed stars and the sun remain unmoved, that the earth revolves about the sun on the circumference of a circle, the sun lying in the middle of the orbit . . .

Archimedes obviously gave little credit to the idea, and it is likely many other Greek philosophers didn't either. Beyond science, Aristarchus and Copernicus were dealing with a similar problem: describing a world that worked differently than popular consensus or common sense dictated. It is not known if Aristarchus was completely alone in his belief, but there is no indication that his theory conflicted with religious doctrine. It is most likely that the Sun-centered solar system was simply too advanced for a consensus of Greek astronomers to accept. Without further collaborative evidence, it was forgotten.

To say that Aristarchus was ahead of his time is one of the biggest understatements in the history of science. It took over a hundred years for the Copernican view of the solar system to become widely accepted. By then, almost 2,000 years had passed since it had first been described by Aristarchus. We give full credit to Copernicus for his paradigm shift, but that credit should be at least shared with Aristarchus. Copernicus even opted to mention Aristarchus in an early draft of his book, but not in the final version. It has been speculated that this was more about validating his own work and less of acknowledging Aristarchus. It is a moot point today as the work of Aristarchus is completely overshadowed by Copernicus.

What little we do know about Aristarchus should make him a legend of science. His two known works are classic examples of theoretical and applied science on the highest level. The story of his lost work is a regrettable example of a valuable theory lost before proven. However, his technique of measuring the distance to the Moon was definitive for thousands of years. The method finally would offer some sort of vindication for Aristarchus as it would eventually lead to an undeniable proof that he and Copernicus were right.

Illuminating the Night

The Moon's motion differs from the other classic celestial orbs. It orbits in predictable circles and doesn't exhibit the retrograde motion seen in the planets. Today, the reason is scientifically trivial. The Moon orbits Earth while the planets orbit the Sun, but this fact is not apparent without some basic assumptions that we take for granted. Without those guiding principles, the view of Copernicus lay mostly dormant for 50 years until Johannes Kepler and Galileo Galilei simultaneously revived it. Each would take a different approach. Kepler believed mathematics was the key to understanding what he called "Celestial Physics," while Galileo documented what he believed to be undeniable evidence using a telescope.

Kepler's first attempt to combine mathematics and astronomy was a curious failure. It can be found in his book, the *Mysterium Cosmographicum*, published in 1596. It was based on the notion that the spacing between the six known planets, which included Earth, was determined by the five platonic solids. Each shape would fill the gap between two different planetary orbits. Although this first attempt didn't succeed, he persevered. His breakthrough finally occurred when he started considering elliptical orbits. This would lead to Kepler's first law of planetary motion:

All planets move in elliptical orbits.

He would later add two other laws that established a relationship between the speed of the planet's motion and its distance from the Sun. While the Moon's orbit was predictable and of little consequence to

Kepler's work, it was a significant part of Galileo's discoveries. First, he noticed details of light and shadow on the Moon and correctly deduced that there were mountains and valleys on its surface. This all but confirmed the idea of the Moon to be an actual world like Earth. He also saw phases of Venus that were like the Moon's, indicating that Venus was circling around the Sun. But the most striking discovery of all came when he detected four new moons orbiting Jupiter. It was the first time that anything had been seen orbiting around something other than Earth.

Galileo immediately published his observations in the *Starry Messenger* in 1610 and used them to support heliocentrism. His continued work slowly would build up an antagonizing relationship with Catholic Church authorities. It came to a head in 1632 when Pope Urban VIII asked Galileo to write a book that unbiasedly compared both views of the solar system. The resulting book, Dialogue Concerning the Two Chief World Systems, did not paint a flattering picture of the geocentric view or those who believed in it. This angered the pope, and Galileo was put on trial the following year.

Kepler did not suffer the same fate as Galileo as he could stay outside the influence of the Roman Catholic Church. Though his life was often hard, he continued to write on a variety of subjects. When Galileo sent him a copy of the *Starry Messenger*, he enthusiastically published his reaction, and followed up with a publication of his own observations. This led to him to develop improvements for his own telescope. Beyond astronomy, Kepler wrote about mathematics, geometry, astrology, and theology, which he believed were all connected. Although he is known for his three laws of planetary motion, his crowning achievement during his lifetime was the *Rudolphine Tables*, a comprehensive reference of planetary positions based on his model of the solar system and the data collected by Tycho Brahe. He had even speculated on gravity, but it was not his primary concern.

There is an uncorroborated account of Galileo dropping two objects with different weights from the famous Leaning Tower of Pisa. If true, Galileo would have demonstrated a basic principle of gravity. It is known that Galileo measured speeds of falling objects and discovered they accelerated uniformly. To honor Galileo's contribution to science, Astronaut David Scott of Apollo 15 simultaneously dropped a feather and hammer on the surface of the Moon. Galileo could not have produced the same effect on Earth, and this same burden of proof also clouded his arguments for the Copernican view. While Galileo felt he had found definitive evidence in favor of Copernicus, his observations equally could have supported the unusual hybrid view of Tycho Brahe.

The story of Galileo and Kepler is both amazing and agonizing for the scientific revolution they continued but ultimately didn't finish. The celestial heavens remained linked to spiritual mysticism with its own set of rules. There was no sense of scale to Kepler's elliptical orbits. No one really knew how big the solar system was or the distance to the stars. Likewise, Galileo's experiments with gravity on Earth were incomplete and disconnected from his observations of the night sky. There was still a missing common link.

Apples and Cannonballs

K epler's work inspired many other astronomers and mathematicians. The French astronomer Ismaël Bullialdus was the first to describe the inverse square law and its connection to the force behind Kepler's laws. Increasing the distance of a planet ten times from the Sun diminishes the effect a hundred times. Beginning in 1679, the English scientist Robert Hooke began some correspondence with Isaac Newton on the inverse square law and its connection to the physical world. Although Newton already was familiar with the rule and its connection to Kepler, the correspondence inspired him to look deeper into the matter. By 1681, Newton had found a mathematical proof that connected Kepler's elliptical orbits to the inverse square law. He then expanded the work into the Principia, his masterpiece of scientific reasoning published in 1687.

Newton's Principia, or *The Mathematical Principles of Natural Philosophy*, is a massive work that marks the beginnings of modern physics. It contains his three laws of motion and his law of gravity. Newton used the Principia to show that the universe could be explained mathematically rather than haphazardly discovered. While Kepler had discovered his laws of planetary motion through mostly trial and error, Newton stated they could have been derived mathematically. He described a stable orbit as a balanced interaction of three basic forces: a spinning force that pushes out, a gravitational force that pulls in, and a force of momentum as an object travels through space. To illustrate, he compared the orbit of the Moon to that of a fast-moving cannonball. Under normal conditions, any cannonball shot from an imaginary mountaintop would fall quickly to Earth, but if a cannonball could be shot fast enough, its velocity could counterbalance the effects of gravity. It would fall but never hit the ground because Earth's surface would curve away from it. It continually would circle Earth just like the Moon. Though he didn't account for air resistance, Newton otherwise was correct. These fundamental forces still apply to the orbits of satellites and spacecraft.

As the understanding of planetary orbits shifted from Ptolemy to Copernicus, the Moon's remained unchanged. It was the only object in the night sky that did orbit Earth, and this fact became useful for Newton. He realized the Moon was the farthest known object to be affected by Earth's gravity. He also knew the approximate distance to the Moon, thanks in part to Aristarchus of Samos, who had proposed the true nature of the solar system nearly 2,000 years earlier. This gave Newton the data he needed to apply mathematics to the orbit of the Moon.

When it comes to Newton's inspiration for gravity, falling apples usually come to mind instead of the Moon, but both are true. He was never hit on the head by a falling apple as it is often portrayed in cartoons and comedies, but he likely was inspired by watching them occasionally fall in a garden. The connection to the Moon probably had more to do with the shape of an apple, which basically is a sphere like the Moon. If the motions of both a falling apple and the orbiting Moon were two responses to the same force, Newton could study the effect of Earth's gravity from two extremely different points in space.

Since Newton knew the distance to the Moon, he easily could calculate the length of its circumference and therefore the speed of the Moon. Since the forward momentum must be equal to the force of gravity, Newton could calculate the force Earth exerted on the Moon. The measured effect of gravity on the ground was already known due to experiments first run by Galileo. By calculating the speed that the Moon needed to maintain its orbit, Newton was able to determine the strength of Earth's gravity at that far distance. It turned out that Earth's effect on the Moon was only 1/3600 as strong as the force on a falling apple. Since Newton knew the Moon was 60 times farther away than an apple, the strength of Earth's gravity matched the inverse square law perfectly. It was proof that Earth's gravity affected both in the same way. The Moon was falling like an apple, but with just enough velocity to keep it permanently in orbit.

A Universal Truth

The Moon helped Newton prove universal gravity, and in return, Newton gave the Moon a new sense of reality. Ordinary physics replaced metaphysical context. The theory of gravity also proved that Earth was a round sphere, and that Earth orbited the Sun. Newton gave the world physical laws that applied equally to objects in the sky and on Earth, and the Moon was critical to that breakthrough. Without the Moon, Newton would have lacked a common reference that existed in the sky but also responded to Earth's gravity.

Within a short time, Newton's universal law of gravity became widely accepted. It was repeatedly tested and proven to be correct with improved observations. In 1672, astronomers Giovanni Cassini and John Flamsteed used variations of stellar parallax, which had eluded Tycho Brahe, to measure the distance to Mars. The result was a solid estimate of the scale of the solar system. In 1751, French astronomers Joseph Lalande and Nicolas-Louis de Lacaille simultaneously recorded the Moon's position as seen from Paris and the Cape of Good Hope on Africa's southern tip. They discovered a shift of seven and half degrees, which allowed them to use trigonometry and calculate the distance to the Moon at 365,000 miles.

The Copernican solar system was a confirmed reality, and the law of gravity would become a valuable tool for finding other objects in space, from the planet Neptune to black holes to exoplanets. Although Einstein's general theory of relativity eventually would give us a deeper understanding of gravity, Newton's basic equation still works in all but the most extreme cases. Einstein himself idolized Newton and simply improved on the idea of using mathematics to describe the nature of the universe.

Newton became the most celebrated scientist of his time. He became the president of the Royal Society and the second Lucasian Professor of Mathematics at Cambridge. While Copernicus, Kepler, Galileo, and many others including Aristarchus had suspected how the universe worked, Newton created undeniable proof. His reputation for being correct was impeccable, and he furiously defended it. A bitter rivalry later would ensue between him and Robert Hooke over credit for the discovery of a law of gravity.

Hooke felt that some of the early work was his, so he should share the credit for the discovery. Newton had acknowledged him and others in the Principia for inspiration but felt the concept of an inverse square law was commonly known and required no further credit. On the other hand, his work was a meticulous mathematical proof which he had labored on alone. The French mathematician Alexis Clairaut later said it was the difference between "truth glimpsed" and "truth demonstrated," and this was what essentially separated Newton from Hooke, and everyone else.

Perhaps the ultimate irony in Newton's life was the Church of England bestowing their highest honor on him by burying him within Westminster Abbey alongside the greatest thinkers of his time. Some of Newton's views on Christianity were slightly unorthodox, and he might not have chosen the honor for himself, but such was the fame of his monumental achievement that even the religious authority of England had to accept it for what it was. The Moon had changed for them as well.

The Moon we see today is the Moon of Newton because Newtonian physics drive our world. It is a Moon of facts and figures that we readily accept as part of our lives, and gravity has become an unquestionable universal truth. Beyond all his scientific discoveries, what Newton gave us most of all was a universal faith in science. Since the days of Newton, the Moon represents our quest for an unambiguous truth. This became especially true during the Apollo Moon missions, where new facts changed our view of the world.

Moon Secret 3: Russia landed on the Moon first.

The Soviet Union successfully landed the first unmanned probe, Luna 2, on the Moon's surface in 1959. It was the beginning of a successful series of unmanned probes, which achieved many milestones in lunar exploration. Long before Apollo 11, the Soviets sent back the first close-up pictures of the Moon and returned the first lunar soil samples, all with unmanned probes. The Soviets also developed a plan for manned lunar missions, but a series of unexpected setbacks finally caused them to abandon the idea.

The Moon

The Moon was but a Chin of Gold
A Night or two ago—
And now she turns Her perfect Face
Upon the World below—

EMILY DICKINSON

FEBRUARY:
A Piece of the Moon

The Storm Moon (English Medieval)

(The improbable story of moon rocks)

Choosing the Moon

n September 12, 1962, President Kennedy, a man remembered for inspiring speeches, delivered one of his best:

> "We choose to go to the Moon in this decade and do the other things, not because they are easy, but because they are hard; because that goal will serve to organize and measure the best of our energies and skills, because that challenge is one that we are willing to accept, one we are unwilling to postpone, and one we intend to win."

It was a warm late summer day as Kennedy stood before a packed college stadium at Rice University and effortlessly mixed visions of the future with jokes about the heat and college football. It had been over a year since he had first proposed sending a man to the Moon, and he had come to Houston, Texas, to get an update from NASA. His speech was a second opportunity to inspire Americans to choose the Moon. By publicly addressing his incredibly audacious plan, Kennedy masterfully reshaped it into an American destiny that it was uniquely suited to achieve. By comparing it to other notably historic achievements, he correctly predicted that the United States would play a key part in one of the greatest events in human history.

It had been less than 20 years since World War II had ended. The memory of a hard-fought victory was still a meaningful generational memory. Young as he was, Kennedy had fought in the war, lost a brother to it, and had succeeded one of its most famous generals in becoming president. He now was poised to take the United States into a new era, but this was more than simple providence. It is no coincidence that the space race occurred during the height of the Cold War. Going to the Moon would be the final focal point of military technologies developed in World War II, and its realization later would inspire a limited de-escalation, and the beginnings of a global community in search of peace. A united Earth would be an unexpected result of humanity reaching for the Moon.

World War II had drastically altered the world technically and politically. Its aftermath triggered the development of massive war industries inside the United States and Soviet Union, which became entrenched in their economies and part of their national identities. Based on rapid improvements to weapons technologies developed during the war, large stockpiles of ICBMs (intercontinental ballistic missiles) quickly dotted the world. Understandably, no one wanted the terrifying experience of Hiroshima and Nagasaki a dozen times over, so nuclear weapons became nuclear deterrents. Their ultimate power was the psychological threat of a potential strike.

Public fear of a missile gap between the two superpowers grew within the United States in the late fifties. Originally arising from exaggerated estimates of the Soviet military strength, the perceived imbalance triggered widespread concern and was used to gain political support in the U.S. When the Soviets successfully launched Sputnik, followed by the launch of Yuri Gagarin as the first man in orbit, the United States could not immediately respond. Americans felt they were falling behind in the eyes of the world, which was unacceptable. In response, Kennedy turned to the newly formed NASA for advice on a next step. The only goal that did not seem imminently achievable by the Soviets was a manned Moon mission. Both countries had sent unmanned probes to the Moon, but sending a human being would require a much more powerful rocket than neither country currently possessed. This would equal the playing field and give NASA time to catch up.

For all its suffering, World War II had oddly gifted humankind everything it needed to go to the Moon. Guided rockets and electronic computers were both developed to win the war. Fueled by a postwar buildup, the rockets would get a lot bigger while the computer components got smaller. Nazi Germany's V2 rocket was the first long-range guided ballistic missile and the first man-made object to enter space. Developed by rocket pioneer Wernher von Braun, its design was the basis for the Redstone rocket used on the first two Mercury missions. Von Braun had surrendered to the United States toward the end of the war. First employed by the United States Army, he was transferred to NASA to work on its Jupiter Rocket series, which was followed by the Saturn V.

Early modern computers were used to break German military codes at Bletchley Park in England, and their success has been credited with shortening the war and saving millions of lives. Incredibly bulky at first, reductions in size would be driven by military needs long before they were commercially available. By 1947, the bipolar transistor was invented to replace the vacuum tubes used by earlier computers. The first integrated circuits or computer chips would follow in 1958, and the Apollo guidance computer was one of the first to use them. Developed for the war and accelerated by the space race, computers are the obvious byproduct of Moon-related technologies. Interconnected with a satellite infrastructure launched by rockets, they have become the backbone of a future world that even Kennedy didn't see.

Some note that Kennedy had little interest in space exploration before addressing the space rivalry with the Soviet Union. This point is often used to dampen the sense of idealism attributed to Kennedy, but it should not diminish his accomplishment. Critics of Kennedy have questioned his legacy and the wasteful expense of going to the Moon. While some suggest the money could have been better spent, there's little reason to suspect much of it would alternatively have gone to better causes. What is beyond doubt is the world gained from a second boom of technology without the massive loss of life from a world war. We can still credit Kennedy for the right reasons and remember him for delivering a visionary speech of the future with his trademarked persuasive elegance.

Sadly, we are forced to consider Kennedy's Moon Speech as both a poetic beginning and ironic end. Shot by an Italian military surplus rifle made during World War II, he became a symbolic victim of the same war industry that prepared the world for going to the Moon. Some suggest that even Kennedy's death was a necessary step toward a manned Moon mission, which is a somber note of how unlikely his plan was.

Kennedy had originally hoped a manned Moon landing could take place within seven years and a likely second term of his administration, but NASA's director James Webb privately warned him it would not be possible. In June 1961, Kennedy asked Soviet Premier Nikita Khrushchev to consider a joint mission to the Moon. The massive expense of Apollo and the possibility of a colossal failure were just two reasons for Kennedy to reconsider his original goal. Going to the Moon was neither politically nor publicly popular. Projects Mercury and Gemini were both successful and would have allowed Kennedy to cancel Apollo while preserving national pride. The shock of Kennedy's assassination changed all of that and sent the United States firmly in the other direction. President Johnson was easily reelected in 1964, and NASA's budget skyrocketed in the following years with little opposition.

During his final United Nations address, Kennedy repeated his invitation to the Soviets for a joint Moon mission. The offer was rejected again. In practical terms, it would have lowered the cost of space exploration for both countries, but it was also a genuine gesture for peace, and the sentiment would endure. As astronauts started traveling to the Moon, they sent back pictures of a world universally shared and without borders. While the United States symbolically conquered the Moon, it was claimed in the name of peace. NASA astronauts speaking from the surface of the Moon would borrow Kennedy's globally optimistic tone for years to come.

The Rise and Fall of the Saturn V

For half a century, the Saturn V remained the only manned rocket powerful enough to have left Earth orbit. First launched as a test on November 9, 1967, its firing has become a quintessential symbol of space flight. Named after its five monstrous F-1 engines, the sky-scraping 363-foot rocket began its journey deceptively slow by clearing the tower at a regal 60 miles per hour. In a dance of physics on a gigantic scale, 7.5 million pounds of thrust struggled to pull 6.2 million pounds of rocket off the launch pad.

NASA would launch 13 Saturn V rockets with a near perfect record, but not all were destined for the Moon. Apollo 4, the first Saturn V, only orbited Earth three times and had no crew. This is a commonly overlooked achievement of the Saturn V. Its guidance was fully automated, and the launch was controlled remotely from mission control.

NASA elected to use Apollo 4 as an "all-up" test, known internally as Operation Big Shot. All components of the Saturn V would be tested in a single unmanned mission. This bold gamble by NASA meant that no one really knew what to expect when the rocket's engines ignited. The launch pad had been specifically based three miles away in anticipation of a tremendous blast. Even at that great distance, the launch forcibly shook the mission control building. In a live broadcast, news anchor Walter Cronkite yelled in excitement over the noise as the building rattled around him and ceiling tiles fell to the ground:

"Our building's shaking! Oh it's terrific...the building's

shaking! This big blast window is shaking! We're holding
it with our hands! Look at that rocket go..."

The brief mission was a flawless success and proved that NASA was
ready for the Moon. At eight and a half hours, it was the shortest Apollo
mission, but within that time it managed to simulate most of the major
steps used in the later manned missions. This included sending an empty
Apollo space capsule beyond Earth's orbit, followed by a reentry and
splashdown.

This preview of the future restored public confidence in the project
while presenting never-before-seen views from outer space. Four special
cameras mounted inside the rocket recorded the famous stage-separation
sequence in slow motion. The footage would be quickly incorporated
into a classic *Star Trek* episode just a few months later and has been
reused countless times since. Another camera mounted in the command
capsule would take the very first high-resolution pictures of Earth from
space.

Apollo 6, NASA's second unmanned test, did not go so well and
is considered only a partial success. It was intended to simulate the
Translunar Injection maneuver needed for setting a course to the Moon,
but engine problems forced a change of plans. Two engines on the second stage failed midway during launch, forcing an extra-long burn of
the remaining three, and the third stage engine refused to reignite when
needed. NASA tried to compensate with the use of the engine on the
Apollo service module, but the result was not much better than that of
Apollo 4.

The most important lesson learned from Apollo 6 was how easy it was
for things to go wrong, and a considerable effort was made to make sure
it wouldn't happen again. Eight successful manned missions followed the
marred Apollo 6, making the Saturn V one of the most reliable rockets
of its time. The two most notable incidents were a pair of lightning
strikes on Apollo 12 shortly after launch and an oxygen tank explosion
aboard the service module of Apollo 13. Neither was directly related to

the design or creation of the Saturn V.

The last Saturn V rocket to be launched had no Apollo designation. By getting to the Moon before its competition, the Saturn V effectively ended the space race, but in doing so became a victim of its own success. The politics of space exploration had shifted. Designed for reaching the Moon first at all costs, the Saturn V was viewed as an overly expensive Moon missile. The Soviets had shifted their focus to orbiting space stations, compelling the United States to follow suit. To quickly adapt, NASA ingeniously converted the third stage of what would have been Apollo 18 into Skylab, the first United States space station.

Adapting the Saturn V into a heavyweight orbital delivery system had been an extended goal of NASA from the start. The extremely reliable first two stages launched Skylab's 130-ton payload into orbit in a matter of minutes, but there would be no funds allocated to build more Saturn V rockets. Unlike Apollo 4, the launch of Skylab in 1973 was a near disaster. Skylab was heavily damaged during launch and required major repairs before it was habitable. Skylab ultimately became a success with three separate crews conducting hundreds of experiments. On its closing mission, NASA parked Skylab into a high orbit hoping it could be later used in conjunction with the future space shuttle program, but the orbit unexpectedly decayed in the late seventies. With no rescue possible from the unfinished space shuttle, Skylab burned up in the atmosphere in 1979.

The final Apollo mission didn't use a Saturn V. Marking a dignified but anticlimactic end to the space race, the joint Apollo–Soyuz mission of 1975 was little more than a meetup in Earth's orbit that didn't require NASA's most powerful rocket. The combined crew appropriately featured Deke Slayton and Alexei Leonov as a tribute to the original Mercury and Vostok space pioneers. It was a bittersweet conclusion, but also an exciting test of things to come. NASA had proved that joint missions were both technically and politically possible. Skylab and Apollo–Soyuz were the first steps toward the more practical International Space Station. The United States turned away from the

Moon, and the remaining Saturn V components would find their way to various space museums.

We now celebrate the short-lived era of giant expendable Saturn V rockets as the technology that took humanity to the Moon, but its secondary achievement is just as important. It was the rocket that allowed us to bring back a part of the Moon. Humanity went on a lunar rock collecting adventure with an average of over 100 pounds (45 kilograms) per mission. Scientists now have the option to look at the Moon with microscopes, and the rocks that Apollo retrieved have changed our understanding of the Moon and Earth.

The Last Man on the Moon

While Neil Armstrong and Buzz Aldrin were making history by being the first humans to walk on the Moon, the Soviet Union had a clever plan to share the spotlight with Apollo 11's Moon landing. They had timed their unmanned Luna 15 probe to land on the Moon around the same time as Neil Armstrong and Buzz Aldrin. Unfortunately, the event was a PR disaster. Luna 15 unceremoniously crashed into a mountainside, just as the astronauts were getting ready to leave.

Luna 16 redeemed the Soviets a year later when it became the first robotic mission to successfully send lunar soil samples back to Earth. After a perfect soft landing, it drilled into the surface of the Moon and placed the collected soil into an upper ascent stage that returned to Earth three days later. It was a brilliant if somewhat late triumph for the Soviet space program, but launching unmanned would never work for the U.S.

Besides limited press, robotic missions had other limitations too. There was no control over what came back to Earth. The soil sample ultimately was determined by wherever Luna 16 landed. The soil sample also was tiny, just under a gram. By comparison, astronauts simply were better at collecting lunar samples in every way. Once on the surface, they simply could walk over to an interesting rock, pick it up, and get it ready to return to Earth. The need to win a political war had oddly but fortuitously given the U.S. a superior rock-retrieval system. Luckily, NASA had a geologist training to be an Apollo astronaut, but he almost didn't get to go.

Harrison Schmitt joined NASA as part of Astronaut Group 4 in 1965. NASA trained future astronauts in groups based on needs for upcoming missions. Known as "The Scientists," the group was selected based on their academic credentials and were not required to have any prior flying experience. NASA would train them if necessary. Among the small cohort of six astronauts, Schmitt was the only one with a geology background. The group had been created in part to encourage support from the scientific community. NASA's research budget was limited, and it needed to draw as much expertise from outside sources as it could. It was also thought that pure scientific research would become the primary goal as later lunar missions became more routine.

With the success of Gemini, NASA rapidly developed an expansion plan for Apollo. With dozens of potential missions, it was quickly realized that they needed to increase the number of astronauts. Group 4 was small and was going to need an extra year of flight training. Group 5 comprised 19 astronauts, all of whom had extensive piloting experience. As Group 4 worked through their extra training, a personnel issue arose when it became apparent that Group 5 was getting preferential treatment for crew assignments. There was an outcry among NASA staff scientists, and Schmitt was reassigned to the backup crew of Apollo 15 to remedy the situation.

Backup crews were part of NASA's larger crew rotation system and routinely rotated to become the prime crew for future missions. Schmitt's new position put him in line to be the lunar module pilot of Apollo 18. After Apollo 18 was cancelled, Schmitt replaced Lunar Module Pilot Joe Engle in a last chance effort to put a geologist on the Moon. He would join Gene Cernan on Apollo 17, making him the last man chosen for a Moon mission. As he exited the lunar module to become the last man to step on the Moon, Schmitt proclaimed the site as:

"A good geologist's paradise if I've ever seen one!"

Schmitt made good on his claim. Of the total 840 pounds (381 kilograms) of moon rocks retrieved by Apollo, over a quarter is owed to the efforts of Apollo 17. Among the many samples he brought back is one called Troctolite 76535, which has been dubbed the most interesting rock returned from the Moon. It was the oldest rock retrieved from the Moon to be unshocked (untainted) by meteorite impact. Extensive tests have revealed the rock formed deep within the Moon at a depth of 47 kilometers. It has given valuable insights into the Moon's core and its early history. Other key breakthroughs in the Moon's origin would come later from the scientific research that Schmitt represented. The last man chosen for Apollo was also its first and only scientist.

As Schmitt entered the lunar module for the last time, Mission Commander Gene Cernan took a moment to reflect on the end of an era with a closing speech:

> "I'd just like to [say] what I believe history will record;
> That America's challenge of today has forged man's des-
> tiny of tomorrow. And, as we leave the Moon at Taurus–
> Littrow, we leave as we came and, God willing, as we shall
> return with peace and hope for all mankind."

Cernan would later write a book called The Last Man on the Moon, a title that he could equally share with Schmitt. His last words from the Moon set an appropriate conclusion to the era and mirrored Kennedy's original speech just 11 years earlier. Placing a man on the Moon originally was driven by fear of war and world domination, but in the end, it led to a revelation about Earth's origin. Without manned missions to collect rocks, we could have never learned what we now know about the Moon, or Earth.

Expensive Rocks

Humanity's time on the Moon was all too brief. The illusion of routine trips to the Moon concluded on December 13, 1972, with a ceremonial end by the crew of Apollo 17. Back on Earth, youth ambassadors from around the world had gathered in Houston to see and hear the event. During the last extravehicular activity (EVA), Schmitt grabbed a 3.0-kilogram piece of coarse-grained basalt rock that he had found earlier and handed it to Cernan for a dedication.

"The promise of the future lies in the young people, not just in America, but the young people all over the world learning to live and learning to work together. In order to remind all the people of the world in so many countries throughout the world that this is what we all are striving for in the future, Jack has picked up a very significant rock...

It's a rock composed of many fragments, of many sizes and many shapes, probably from all parts of the Moon, perhaps billions of years old. But fragments of all sizes and shapes—and even colors—that have grown together to become a cohesive rock...

[W]e'd like to share a piece of this rock with so many of the countries throughout the world. We hope that this will be a symbol of what our feelings are, what the feelings of the Apollo Program are, and a symbol of mankind: that we can live in peace and harmony in the future."

The rock known as lunar basalt 70017 returned to Earth and became the Goodwill Rock. Samples were later cut off and sent to 135 countries and all 50 states. Unfortunately, a large number of those samples have gone missing with some feared to be stolen. Due to the incredible expense of the Apollo program, NASA has estimated the value of a moon rock to be $100,000 an ounce. Very few are owned privately, making them even rarer, but in most cases the missing rocks are the likely victim of clerical error. After the public excitement for Apollo memorabilia died down, the rocks lost their appeal. While their monetary value is debated, the scientific knowledge gained from them is priceless.

Not all discoveries turned out to be as revolutionary as expected, and some discoveries turned out to be false leads. Earlier testing of Apollo 11 samples revealed three minerals never seen before on Earth: Armalcolite, Pyroxferroite, and Tranquillityite, suggesting an exotic lunar geology. To honor the discovery, Armalcolite was named after the Apollo 11 crew, Armstrong, Aldrin, and Collins, but the premise about unique lunar minerals turned out to be false. In time all three were discovered on Earth. Similarly, the aptly named Genesis Rock found by Apollo 15 was once suspected to be part of the Moon's original crust and would provide valuable data about the Moon's creation. Further testing revealed it to be not as old as originally thought, but its prophetic name stuck.

Eventually, the most important insights about the Moon did not come from individual samples. The Moon's geology turned out to be far simpler than Earth's. Most moon rocks are composed of only four minerals and seven elements and completely missing many elements commonly found on Earth. While this presented an unexpected mystery, radio isotope testing created a bigger one. All rocks in the solar system have a unique oxygen isotope signature that identifies where they originally were formed. When moon rocks were subjected to an isotope signature test, they were found to be identical to rocks found on Earth. This single result had profound implications. Such a coincidence was impossible and could lead to only one inescapable conclusion. The Moon and Earth were once joined as part of the same object.

What Cernan had said about the Goodwill Rock was a poetic tribute to the Moon and Earth's past. Now separated and distinctly different, they had once been part of the same rock. His analogy meant to encourage a global society had an extra hidden meaning. After striving for peace, humanity had found unity between Earth and the Moon.

The Greatest Event in History

The oldest known Earth rock was discovered in a moon rock. This cryptic statement perfectly illustrates the common history shared between the two worlds. Due to constant tectonic activity and surface erosion, very few rocks on Earth are older than 3 billion years, but an embedded Earth meteorite found in a sample collected by Apollo 14 known as Big Bertha is over 4 billion years old. Only recently discovered in 2019, the rock's Earth origin has been confirmed by the high content of minerals not found on the Moon. It is the only known example of an Earth-based meteorite.

At nearly 20 pounds (9 kilograms), Big Bertha was one of the largest rocks collected by Apollo. Named after the giant guns and artillery shells fired during the great world wars, Big Bertha was a nickname originally used by German soldiers in World War I to describe a massive 16.5-inch howitzer that could fire 120-pound shells over five miles. After the war, the name became synonymous with any big gun. The irony of a significant lunar specimen named after a giant war gun encapsulates Apollo's past connection to war. The program was an adaptation of weapons technology and manned by former military personnel. Humanity's greatest achievement would always be tied to its greatest war.

During the first half of the 20th century, two competing scientific theories explained the Moon's origin. In simple terms, the Moon had either been a captured asteroid or formed independently from leftover stellar material. Both theories were well respected and still explain most of the moons in our solar system, but neither theory could explain the identical isotope signatures linking moon and earth rocks. The Moon and Earth had a common origin, which meant a new theory needed to be developed.

In 1975, William Hartman and Donald Davis first published the Giant Impact Theory. The theory proposed that while Earth was quite young and mostly molten with a newly formed crust, a huge asteroid about the size of Mars struck it with a glancing blow. Rather than destroying Earth outright, the impact swept extensive amounts of Earth's crust out into space. This new material would eventually coalesce into a ring and then form into the Moon we know today. Even though such an extreme event would have seemed unlikely, it explained the data from the test results almost perfectly, and the basic idea behind the Giant Impact Theory remains unchallenged to this day. The theoretical asteroid was even given a name, Theia, after the Greek goddess who gave birth to the Moon.

Since the original proposition, several unsolved questions have led to alternate variations of the collision. Where are the remnants of Theia, and why was there such a lack of many common earth minerals on the Moon? In 2012, scientists suggested a direct collision was a better explanation than the glancing blow. Theia mostly was destroyed by the impact, and what little remained was equally shared between the Moon and Earth. It also has been suggested that Theia's isotope signature may be so close to Earth's that any remaining residue matter would be hard to find. While alternate details continue to evolve, the core idea of a giant impact remains. There's little doubt that the Moon was created out of the most dramatic geological event that Earth could have endured.

The Moon is now part of human history, but our accomplishment has given us a better understanding of Earth's history. Without astronauts picking up moon rocks, we might never have learned about the origin of Earth because we would have lacked the physical evidence. Considering Apollo's military origin, it stands as a unique lesson learned from war. The Moon is part of us, flung far out into space billions of years ago. It is a constant reminder of that first significant event in Earth's history, the biggest and oldest piece of Earth that we can see with our own eyes.

PART 2:

SPRING
The Moon and Life

The Moon's influence on our lives is subtle, constant, and mostly unknown. From prehistoric times, it has taught us how to measure time, but our most critical connection to the Moon is far older and lies deep within our world.

March: Forever Spring
April: The Eternal Sentinel
May: The Mystic Warrior

Moon Secret 4: A Harvest Moon can last for days.

All full moons rise exactly at sunset, but on successive nights the Moon rises slightly later each night. The gap between one moonrise and the next varies depending on the time of year and the location of the observer. In the Northern Hemisphere, the gap is at its shortest at the beginning of autumn and, depending on the latitude, it can be as little as ten minutes. Historically, this has meant that for several nights after a full moon in autumn, a near full moon would rise before the sky had a chance to go dark. Farmers could continue to take advantage of a few extra hours of light, and the Harvest Moon took its name from the busy time it helped to illuminate.

Waiting—Afield at Dusk
And in the antiphony of afterglow
And rising full moon, sit me down
Upon the full moon's side of the first haycock
And lose myself and so many alike.

ROBERT FROST

MARCH:
Forever Spring

The Sleepy Moon (Chinese)

(The legend of the Moon and the never-ending cycle of seasons)

The Lost Name of the Moon

The Moon has no name. It's simply called "the Moon," and this might seem trivial unless you're an astronomer or science-fiction writer. The official count of moons in the solar system has surpassed 200 and probably will continue to grow, and all but the most recently discovered have given names. As the number has increased, the word "moon" is more of a classification and less of a proper name. Somehow, the Moon got left behind without a name of its own, and no other object in the night sky has this problem. There is no discovered galaxy, comet, or asteroid that was ever referred to by its basic description alone. The Sun is a star, but the Moon is a moon. This also is usually true in other languages, as Galileo would have referred to the moons of Jupiter as *lune di Giove*, and the Moon as *Luna*.

Even if it were argued that the Moon doesn't need a name because it's likely to be the topic of most moon conversations, it is still slightly odd to be calling the Moon a moon. This ambiguity has been occasionally remedied in science fiction where the Moon would be one of many moon locations. Robert Heinlein, who wrote many science fiction novels involving the Moon, set the standard by using the name Luna to distinguish it from other moons in the solar system, but this is not an official name.

Moon names have a long and confusing history that began shortly after new moons were first discovered. In 1609, Galileo saw moons orbiting Jupiter. He originally named them in honor of his patrons, the powerful Medici family, but he wasn't alone in his discovery. The German astronomer Simon Marius discovered the same moons independently and possibly on the same night as Galileo, arguably giving him equal naming rights. Taking a suggestion from Johannes Kepler, he named them after lovers of the Greek god Zeus. Galileo didn't like the idea. He proposed a neutral numbering system that stayed in place for centuries. Moons simply were numbered based on the order of their discovery. As more moons were discovered, Galileo's system became increasingly less desirable. In 1847, British astronomer John Herschel named the seven known moons of Saturn after giants or titans from Greek mythology, leading astronomers to return to naming moons as they were discovered. A formal naming system finally was adopted by the International Astronomical Union in 1973.

In the end, Kepler won. Galileo still gets credit for discovering the moons, but they now bear the names that Marius and Kepler chose: Io, Europa, Ganymede, and Callisto, all lovers of Zeus. Combining the planet Jupiter, a Roman god, with moons named from Greek mythologies might seem like a mismatch, but it was perfectly acceptable. The Romans had frequently adopted Greek myths as their own, making Jupiter and Zeus essentially the same character.

Kepler's idea for the names was also an extremely practical solution that could apply to other moons as well. Similar relationships in mythology represented astronomical connections such as planets and their moons, and there was no shortage of names. Further discovered moons around Jupiter expanded on the earlier precedent with names of Zeus' children, lovers, or other special favorites. Similar naming conventions followed for the moons of other planets, and with only a couple exceptions, Greek and Roman mythology became a standard naming resource. Eventually mythological characters from a variety of cultures would live on in the night skies of modern astronomy.

It was during this time that the Moon came closest to having a name of its own. Updated views of astronomy were inspiring revised maps of the solar system. The Sun was now the center, with everything else revolving around it with equal distinction. This view predictably leads to the concept of a "plurality of worlds." If the Moon and other planets were like Earth, they should be seen as other worlds. It also followed that

Earth and the Moon should be treated as other planets and given similar names. Natural philosopher John Wilkins presented the argument for a plurality of worlds in his book *The Discovery of a World in the Moone*, published in 1638, and followed up with *A Discourse Concerning a New World and Another Planet* in 1640. The cover page of his second book illustrates a failed attempt to give scientific names to both Earth and the Moon. Labeled along with the other planets, Earth and the Moon are designated as Ceres the Roman goddess of nature, and her daughter Proserpina, the goddess of spring.

Even though Wilkins was a popular writer and a founding member of the Royal Society, the names never fell into general use. They would have been perfect choices, and the mother–daughter relationship matched the scientific naming convention already established by the moons of Jupiter. In the 1800s, the names would be repurposed for newly discovered asteroids, and the chance for the Moon to have its own name would be gone for good. Ceres became the first and largest known asteroid, but Proserpina was fated to be the name of a far less significant asteroid, totally unconnected to Ceres.

It is a shame that these names were wasted on unrelated asteroids when they could have captured a unique connection between Earth and the Moon. Beyond the simple family connection, the name Proserpina also would represent the critical part the Moon plays in helping Earth maintain regular seasons. From within the myth of the origin of spring, comes a hint of the Moon's beneficial influence over the seasons.

Like many Roman myths, the story of Ceres and Proserpina was adopted from the Greeks, who knew them as Demeter and Persephone. Hades, the god of the Underworld, steals away Persephone to become his wife. Filled with loss and grief, Demeter searches endlessly for Persephone and abandons Earth, allowing all life to wither away. Eventually, an arrangement is made to allow Persephone to return, but only for part of the year. She must regularly return to the Underworld, and this repeated journey explained the never-ending cycle of the seasons. When Persephone stayed with her mother, Demeter responded with joy by making Earth lush and green, but when Persephone was gone, Demeter's sadness caused winter to return.

Earth and the Moon have a similar relationship to the Grecian goddesses of old. They spin around each other, forming a strong gravitational bond, and the strength of that connection prevents Earth's axis from being swayed by the gravitational influence of other planets. Just as Ceres was lost without her daughter, Earth's axis would wander without the Moon's presence. The cycle of spring would be broken, and all life would suffer and perish. The Moon doesn't just mark the passing of the seasons; it actually helps maintain them. In doing so, it represents a hidden connection to life that we have often given it symbolically through other traditions.

Strawberries and Honey

In space, the Moon is one of many moons, but on Earth it's a marker of seasonal change with each full moon name denoting a different time of the year. The Moon may not have a name of its own, but a full moon has many names depending on the season.

During midsummer months, the Sun climbs to its highest point in the sky, but at night there is an opposite phenomenon. The Moon appears low in the sky and stays close to the horizon. In the Northern Hemisphere, this occurs in June when half of the planet tilts toward the Sun, but that same tilt points it away from the Moon at night. Full moons during this time often have a memorable orange glow. An explanation behind the coloring is the same as when we see an orange sunrise or sunset. By staying closer to the horizon, bluer moonlight is filtered out by the atmosphere, leaving a memorable orange-yellow hue. This special golden moon has inspired its own name and is often called a Honey Moon in Europe and a Strawberry Moon in North America.

Today, the age-old tradition of named full moons continues in our modern society as a welcomed link to an idyllic past. In the West and Northern Hemisphere, the names are mostly a mixture of American Indian culture with influences of European folklore. These names were further readjusted by colonies in the Southern Hemisphere, where the seasons are reversed and often combined with pre-existing indigenous names. This has led to a complex array of overlapping full moon names, but they remain tied to a specific seasonal event. Those meanings are less pertinent today, but their continued use represents a human desire to remain connected to nature and the past. This need has impacted the names themselves as reinterpretations have often changed their original meaning.

The shifting lore of full moon names is perhaps illustrated best in the origin of the name "Blue Moon." That term originally was intended for an extra full moon that didn't have a name. The expression "Once in a Blue Moon" had once meant an impossible occurrence, but it changed in the 17th century to become a very rare event. The Catholic Church of England probably influenced this change as they labored to calculate religious holidays based around full moons. Their system was based on 12 full moons a year, but a 13th full moon was a regular and unwelcome occurrence. As it interfered with the calculations of Easter and Lent holidays, it was called a Lenten Moon, but was also referred to as a "betrayer" or *belewe* in Old English and seen as a bad omen.

The name "Betrayer" was possibly a biblical reference to Judas, the 13th guest at the Last Supper who betrayed Jesus Christ. This is also a source of the unlucky superstition surrounding the number 13. Over time, it's likely that the word *belewe* was transposed with "blue," whose Old English spelling was *blwe* but pronounced similarly. This led to the first astronomical definition of a Blue Moon as being part of a season that contained an extra fourth full moon instead of the usual three. The third full moon of such a season was considered the odd one out and called "Blue." This allowed the other 12 full moons of the year to keep their regular respective names.

The definition of a Blue Moon largely shifted to be a figurative expression until amateur astronomy revived it in the 20th century, where it once again changed thanks to another misinterpretation. In 1946, a *Sky and Telescope* article titled *"Once in a Blue Moon"* by James Pruett concluded that if there were 13 full moons in a year, one month naturally would contain two full moons, and therefore the second full moon of that month was the Blue Moon. Ironically, the same magazine had used the original definition in a question-and-answer column back in 1937, but the new answer stuck. This is now the commonly accepted definition, which has little to do with the original meaning. Its popularity is credited to a 1980s radio show on astronomy and being used as an answer in a *Trivial Pursuit* game around the same time.

The Strawberry Moon is another case of human-influenced transposition, and its origin is more complex than suspected. It's the most well-known full moon name commonly attributed to American Indians, specifically the Algonquian who lived in the New England area during European colonization. While there's no dispute of the connection to American Indian culture, the exact details of how the Strawberry Moon became an Americanized nickname aren't totally clear. The Algonquian were in fact one of many tribes living in the same area, and each had their own unique name for a full moon in high summer. While other tribes, notably the Sioux (who lived hundreds of miles away on the Great Plains), used the name Strawberry Moon, the equivalent Algonquian name translates to "Corn on the hill."

The most likely path the Strawberry Moon took to enter American culture came through Daniel Beard and his book *The American Boy's Book of Signs, Signals and Symbols*, printed in 1918. Beard was the founder of the Sons of Daniel Boone, which would later become the Boy Scouts of America. His book was intended as a reference guide of natural history and American heritage. In the book, Beard listed the Strawberry Moon as the American Indian name for a full moon in June but added that names for full moons vary from tribe to tribe and that his list was an amalgamation based on his intuition. Not long after Beard's book appeared, the Farmers' Almanac of Maine started printing a similar list of full moon names, which it also attributed to the Algonquian. The list differed slightly from Beard's, but the Strawberry Moon was still the full moon of June. Although the implied origin of the full moon names was inaccurate, the tradition stuck and was never further contested. When a revived interest of American Indian culture occurred during the 1980s, the Strawberry Moon name gained new popularity and its origin, which was assumed to be correct, was generalized as American Indian.

The European term Honey Moon also has an unexpected origin. It's commonly assumed that the tradition is directly connected to a full moon in June, a traditionally preferred time for a wedding. It's also assumed to have a long association to the wedding ceremony, but neither one is exactly true. The earliest mention of any kind in English literature was in 1542, where Samuel Johnson warns that the early "tenderness and pleasures" of a married couple's love may quickly fade like the waning moon. By the 1600s, a "honeymoon" finally referred to the blissful first month of a new couple's marriage, but its meaning as a post-marriage holiday didn't start until 1791. It finally became more popular in the 1800s as more newlyweds could afford to travel.

Other purported origins of the honeymoon, like the Viking Mead Moon, are doubted by historians today. A clue to the misunderstanding of its origin comes from its early symbolic usage. The word "honey-moon" was idolized in poems and plays long before it became an actual tradition. What is still romantic for us today was also romantic for people of our past, and longing for a past connection can often produce a fictional one that wasn't there. Nostalgia alone can start a new tradition, which in time becomes part of our cultural history. The Moon's seasonal patterns remind us of simpler times and living in harmony with nature. Using a name for the Moon borrowed from folklore strengthens our connection to the past and satisfies a basic need for continuity, but it also highlights the Moon's connection to the seasons.

A Matter of Degrees

We routinely express patterns of life in mythical terms, but seasons on Earth are strictly determined by simple math. Earth spins on a tilted axis of 23.4 degrees, and that angle is the essence of seasonal change. The tilt is independent of Earth's orbit, so in June the Northern Hemisphere is slightly tilted toward the Sun, and six months later the opposite is true. That small continual swing has been the driving force behind the seasons on Earth for millions of years, and life has continually adapted to that pattern.

Going farther back than any myth, we have marked the summer and winter solstices by the Sun's high and low points in the sky, but the Moon's presence is also a key part of the seasons. Rotational tilt varies from planet to planet and can be shifted by gravitational forces. Mercury and Venus have virtually no tilt in their rotation due their proximity to the Sun. Its gravity acts as a stabilizing force. For Earth, the Moon handles that role.

Taking advantage of the benefits of one season and guarding against the harshness of another is the very essence of survival for most species. Those life-forms that cope the best are the ones most likely to thrive and produce future generations. Seasonal changes are part of a natural test to see which creatures are best equipped to survive, so the Moon is also part of that process.

Earth's tilt gives us more than just seasons; it shapes the way we think about life. It is hard to imagine what life would be like without seasons. If Earth's axis had no tilt, like the planets Mercury and Venus, there would be no seasonal change. There would be no spring thaw and no autumn fall, and no reassuring lesson about life, death, and rebirth. Once again, the Moon can be given full credit for maintaining Earth's gentle lopsided tilt. If the tilt of Earth's axis was a higher angle than 23.4 degrees, the seasonal changes would become much more drastic. If Earth rotated on its side like the planet Uranus, half the planet would bake in continual sunlight while the other half would be plunged into a frozen darkness, and the two halves would constantly swap every six months. Most types of life on Earth could not endure such extreme temperature changes.

The only worse condition than a harsh tilt would be a planet with a constantly shifting one. Such a wobbly planet would be forever shifting from one seasonal pattern to the next. Even though such changes could take millions of years, it would still be a struggle for any life to adapt. By coincidence, Mars has a tilt similar to Earth's at 25.19 degrees, but it has shifted wildly in the past from almost zero to nearly 60 degrees. Meanwhile, material studies of earth rocks have shown that Earth's axis has hardly changed in millions of years, but simulations suggest Earth's axis could swing as much as 10 to 30 degrees without the Moon.

Earth's original tilt remains unknown. It was likely fluctuating like Mars. It was forever changed 4.5 billion years ago with the giant impact of the planetoid Theia and the resulting creation of the Moon. Once Earth and the Moon settled, the axle tilt of Earth was set and would become regulated by the Moon. Ever since that time, the Moon has given Earth predictability, and life has continually adapted to it. As life has become more complex over many eras, it has developed directly in response to those predictable patterns. The more complex a life-form, the more dependent it becomes on a predictable environment that includes the climate. Seasonal plants and trees match their growth cycles to seasonal changes, and animals that depend on those same plants for food and shelter adjust their reproductive and migration patterns for their best chance of survival. Habits of squirrels and other animals learned from childhood become metaphors for how we deal with seasons and life.

Despite gravitational influences, Earth's rotational axis stays extremely stable and hasn't changed more than a degree in a million years. Life on Earth has adapted to the changing seasons with complementary patterns, and those patterns become part of the season itself. Cycles of growth, rest, renewal, and reproduction are all tied to the seasons, and early humans learned to read these signs as a matter of their survival. Winter solstice and the return of spring were a time to celebrate as the cycle was renewed. There was a great psychological reassurance that better times were just around the corner, and our myths eventually would capture that sentiment. We still see winter as a metaphor for the inevitable end only to be followed by a renewal in the spring.

Almost Twins

When our Moon is compared in size to the moons of other planets, very few come close. The giant moons of Jupiter, Ganymede, Calisto, Io, and Europa are similar in size, but only Ganymede is larger, being about twice as big. The only other significantly large moon is Saturn's largest moon Titan, which is about 50 percent bigger than Earth's moon. It makes sense that Jupiter and Saturn would have the biggest moons, but their moons are relatively tiny when compared to the planets they orbit. The massive Ganymede is 1,000 times smaller than Jupiter. This makes Earth's moon unique. Compared to Earth, the Moon is one-sixth the size. Its combined mass and relatively close orbit gives the Moon a stronger gravitational influence on Earth than any other body in the solar system. This is easily seen in the tidal effect of the Moon on the oceans. The Sun's effect is only a third as strong and the other planets essentially have none.

When two orbiting objects in space are close in mass, they have a shared gravitational effect on each other. They spin around in an orbital dance and are known as a binary system. The asteroid 90 Antiope is one example. Discovered in 1866 and named after the daughter of the Greek god Ares, it was later discovered in the year 2000 to be two nearly identical twin asteroids orbiting each other. It is now referred to as a double asteroid. The asteroid pair only have a 2 percent difference in their masses, so their gravitational pull on each other is almost identical. The result is that they orbit around a center point known as a barycenter like a pair of rocks tied together with an imaginary piece of string.

SECRETS OF THE MOON

Double (or binary) asteroids are part of a larger group of astronomical objects called minor-planet moons. Unlike their planetary cousins, they are a lot closer in size to their orbital parents. Some, like 90 Antiope, are so close that they begin to challenge the definition of what a moon is, but most resemble asteroids with smaller moons orbiting around them. Asteroid 243 Ida and its moon Dactyl is a good example with a size ratio of 20 to 1. The asteroid was originally discovered in 1884 and named after the Crete nymph that raised Zeus. The Galileo probe detected the much smaller moon Dactyl in 1993 during a flyby of Ida. Since Galileo had been the first person to discover new moons, this was a surprising and somewhat ironic discovery considering the probe's name. Galileo mission member Ann Harch found it while reviewing images sent back by the probe, making it the first asteroid moon to be found using images sent back from a probe, and the first and so far only moon discovered by a woman.

While not as similar in mass to the identical twins of 90 Antiope, 243 Ida and Dactyl still are considered a binary asteroid because they orbit around a common center point, or barycenter, that's somewhere between the two. Every pair of objects in space has a barycenter, but typically this central point is buried deep inside the larger object. This usually is seen in moons and their planets where the small gravitational influence of the moon is only powerful enough to nudge the planet slightly off its center. Pluto is a notable exception. Its largest moon, Charon, is about half the diameter and one-eighth the mass. This gives the orbits of Pluto and Charon a lopsided wobble that favors the heavier Pluto.

The Moon also gives Earth a significant wobble, but not as severe as Pluto's. Earth and the Moon are nowhere near the twins of 90 Antiope, but they form an even rarer combination. The barycenter for Earth and the Moon is only 1,000 miles below Earth's surface, making them close to a twin system. Rather than being twins, a better family analogy would be a parent and child, spinning around in a tidal dance. Once again, Earth and the Moon are well matched to their lost Greek names of Ceres and

Proserpina because they represent the mother-daughter symbol better than any other planet and moon. Even if the Moon will never be known by that name, it still plays its part perfectly. An endless series of spring seasons flow from its dependable orbit.

A Goddess Returns

Disconnected from the Moon, the classic tale of Proserpina remains embedded in our culture. Great masters, from Bernini to Rubens, have captured her plight in sculpture and painting. It is arguably the best-known myth of all time, and its high drama of an abducted young heroine has become a common plot device in modern storytelling, being adapted into many popular forms from Snow White to Princess Leia. The story also endures as a celebration of the persistence of life and a connection to the past. Even without its long-lost name of Proserpina, the Moon still is associated with many Greek goddesses—Luna, Selene, Artemis, and Diana to name a few. With a newly updated theory of how the Moon was formed comes yet another Greek connection with Hestia, goddess of the hearth.

While the concept of the Giant Impact Theory for the Moon's origin is still widely accepted, several key discrepancies of data have challenged the science community to develop a better theory. The original model of Theia colliding with Earth suggested a large amount of the Moon should have come from Theia, perhaps as high as 70 percent. But initial studies of moon rocks revealed the Moon to be almost identical to Earth. This would mean that Theia had to be almost identical to Earth, or the Giant Impact Theory was wrong. Scientists have continued to adjust the theory mostly on this one issue, with the type of impact being the biggest variable. One update suggests that instead of a glancing blow, Earth may have come close to being pulverized into a liquid state.

A new variation of the giant impact known as the Synestia Theory was introduced in 2012 by Sarah Stewart and Simon Lock. This stated that the impact caused Earth to form into a fast-spinning, molten donut-shaped blob. In this liquid state, the material of the Theia aster-oid and the original Earth were equally distributed, which explains why there's very little trace of Theia left. The Moon formed within the ring of the donut, possibly out of several smaller moons that eventually coalesced into the Moon. In fact, this theory has the Moon forming several hundred years before Earth solidified, making the Moon slightly older. This early planetary state is dubbed within the theory as a Synestia or new Hestia. This coined term references back to the Greek goddess known for her fiery hearth.

Hestia was a sister of Demeter and aunt to Persephone or the Roman Proserpina, which keeps this latest story of the Moon in the family. The theory suggests that Synestia-like impacts might be a common way to create large moons, which might be confirmed by astronomers in the future by the discovery of other Synestia. Whether Hestia is the final goddess associated with the Moon is too soon to tell. The new theory must face the same scientific scrutiny that the original theory did. While alternate theories continue to grow from inconsistencies of the original theory, other explanations also arise. A new study of the minute water particles in moon rocks suggest a slight but measurable difference in the Moon's chemistry after all, suggesting it might comprise up to 40 percent of Theia.

The Moon's origin story continues to be unveiled, but what we have learned adds a new irony to its mystique. The Moon nurtures our sea-sons, but has no seasons of its own, just a long day and night that lasts a month. In the authentic tradition of a Greek tragedy, our nameless Moon performs the ultimate selfless act. It's a lifeless place that makes life on Earth possible. Spring returns every year because of the Moon's dependable orbit, and that fact instills a lesson of hope and faith in all of us. The concept of renewal is a gift from the Moon as an eternal spring comes from an eternal Moon.

Moon Secret 5: A Month lasts 29 and a half days.

As seen from Earth, the Moon takes 29.53 days to complete a lunar cycle, going from one full moon to the next. This fractional number was well known even in ancient civilizations, and it made constructing lunar based calendars very difficult. It made little sense for a month to last a fractional number of days. A simple solution was to vary the length of each calendar month by one day and alternate between 30 and 29 days, sometimes still referred to as full and hollow months. Even though modern calendars have added extra days, this alternating pattern of long and short months is still in place today.

Fragment: "To the Moon"
Art thou pale for weariness
Of climbing heaven and gazing on the earth,
Wandering companionless
Among the stars that have a different birth,—
PERCY BYSSHE SHELLEY

APRIL:
The Eternal Sentinel

The Blood Moon (Southern Hemisphere)

(The Moon's epic journey through time and civilization)

Moon Watchers

I n 1968, the aptly timed classic film *2001: A Space Odyssey* debuted in theaters as NASA raced to complete its epic task of sending a man to the Moon. Based on Arthur C. Clarke's short story The Sentinel, the movie begins with the discovery of the famed black monolith by an early humanoid, known in the book as Moon-Watcher. The experience expands his mind to conceive of weapons made from animal bones capable of hunting prey and killing enemies. When Moon-Watcher realizes the potential of his new power, he celebrates by flinging a bone high in the air. As it falls, the film cuts in a classic cinematic moment to that of a similarly shaped orbiting nuclear weapons platform, and the audience leaps forward in time to a fictional version of the year 2001.

As the story unfolds, humanity moves on toward its second encounter with a monolith. This time it's buried under the Moon's surface. Any memory of the original monolith from over 300,000 years before is long since gone, and yet the sentinel triggers a similar primal response. The moment of contact ends anticlimactically with no gifts of knowledge for the humans that find it. Unprompted, it sends a brief mysterious radio signal toward the outer solar system, and then returns to its inert state. This monolith on the Moon has simply been waiting for humankind to arrive.

The two monoliths represent bookends in the story of humanity and a full circle in its relationship to the Moon. The dawn of time begins with Moon-Watcher making sense of his environment and using it as a tool. His far-off descendants eventually will extend that ability to travel into space. Their first destination and their first new home is the Moon. Mirroring the achievements of the Apollo program, the signal from the second monolith is a symbolic notification that humanity has reached a dawn of a new age. Remove the character of the monolith and replace it with the Moon, and the story of humankind reads the same. Our time on Earth begins and ends with the Moon.

There have been countless generations of real Moon-Watchers spanning time from one era to the next, each building on knowledge of earlier watchers. While some details of the earliest milestones remain unclear, they still represent a chain of discovery and improved application. As we learned to measure time, the Moon became the real sentinel of humankind. While not acting like the fictional monolith, it still played a key role in the development of our civilization. From that first terrestrial step until our eventual first step on the Moon, our society has moved forward at an ever-quickening pace. Every stage of its development can be marked with the need to measure time at a finer precision until we can now measure the Moon's motion to a fraction of a second.

The story of human history is one of progressive refinement. Unlike 2001, the birth of our civilization didn't begin in an instant, but it likely happened slowly at night as the Moon played a crucial part in those early stages. Its orbit has remained a constant throughout history, and its phases and motion are some of the most conspicuous and consistent patterns in nature. There's substantial evidence human beings were observing the Moon and calculating time tens of thousands of years before the earliest known calendars appeared. Calendars were not an invention of ancient civilizations, but merely an adaptation of what was already known.

The Time of the Moon

Thirty-two thousand years ago, the Aurignacian people were watching the Moon and using it to organize their lives. Exact dates from that time are unknown and wouldn't exist for tens of thousands of years, but calendars and recorded history came from their understanding. They had left Africa thousands of years earlier and spread all over Europe. We know about them today from the carvings they left behind. One carved bone found in the Abri Blanchard rock shelter in southwestern France shows they understood the Moon well enough to construct what has been called the earliest lunar calendar. The markings on the bone are grouped into sets of 29, or the number of days between full moons. It suggests that its creators possessed both counting and astronomical knowledge. Paleontologist Alexander Marshack originally devised this interpretation in 1973, and it received a fair amount of criticism when first presented. Further study suggests the markings were deliberate and that Marshack was right.

Without a written language, details of early human developments can be hard to establish. There are only hints of lunar calendars, but they appear frequently enough to suggest they existed tens of thousands of years ago. More details of the Aurignacian culture can be found in cave paintings. They are an iconic symbol of the people we often refer to as cave dwellers. Cave paintings are found all over the world and date between 15,000 and 30,000 years ago, but the "Louvre" of cave painting is located within the Lascaux cave in France containing 6,000 distinct images. Among the sophisticated paintings of bull, deer, and auroch are collections of geometric shapes, some of which have also been interpreted as phases of the Moon. Organized into sets of 14 or 28, they are possibly the work of an artist recording the changing Moon over progressive nights. If true, they would be the oldest known drawings of the Moon.

More concrete evidence for ancient lunar calendars has been found in a field outside of Aberdeenshire in northern Scotland. All that remains now is a row of pits, but it has been determined that they were used for observations of the Moon and Sun. Predating Stonehenge by thousands of years, the site has two important features connecting it to known calendars of ancient history: It tracked the phases of the Moon and could identify the winter solstice. Following the Moon had been established for perhaps thousands of years before, but synchronizing with the winter solstice was a new critical key to an accurate calendar. Twelve lunar phases don't perfectly align to a complete year. Depending on the Moon alone would lead to seasonal drift. A lunar calendar needs to be realigned with the seasons every year, and this same concept would be seen thousands of years later in the calendars of the ancient world. The Assyrians, for example, would begin their year with the first crescent moon after the spring equinox.

By the time of Stonehenge, the ability to track the Sun and Moon was well established. The site was built in phases over thousands of years, but the last stages clearly demonstrate the ability to track the Sun and Moon and the desire to make that ability permanent. Like the pits of Aberdeenshire, many of its stones were aligned to mark the sunrise of the summer solstice. The point of the northernmost moonrise was also marked, indicating that timing the Moon still played an important part in that society. By this time, tracking the Sun was essentially universal, and there are sites like Stonehenge all over the world.

One of the latest discoveries to confirm that ancient astronomy went beyond Stonehenge is the Nebra Sky Disk discovered in central Germany in 1999. Dated to around 1600 B.C., its creation aligns with some of the last work done on Stonehenge. Made of copper and inlaid with gold, it is the oldest known depiction of the night sky. Two phases of the Moon are prominently displayed in the center of the disk surrounded by stars, including the constellation of the Pleiades. While mostly a visual sky reference, markings on the side reveal it could also determine summer and winter solstices as well. Like Stonehenge, its creation marks a transitional point in time. From China to the Maya and the Assyrians, ancient civilizations appeared all over the world. The first calendars and recorded history would soon take over, and the prehistory phase of our culture largely would be lost. We have only recovered fragments of that time, but calendars predate history, and the Moon inspired us to start counting time.

The Missing Days

I n the year 117 A.D., the Roman Empire reached its height of expansion as the reign of Emperor Trajan ended. Over a long period, the empire had grown to completely encircle the Mediterranean Sea and included the ancient civilizations of Babylon, Egypt, and Greece, as well as a great deal of what would later become Great Britain. It was the last great empire of the ancient world and the first to use a calendar system that we could easily recognize today. In fact, the Roman expansion ended precisely on August 10 of that year with the succession of Emperor Hadrian, who was better remembered for building things rather than conquering them. Hadrian's Wall in northern England famously marks the end of the Roman expansion.

The similarity between the Roman calendar and our current one is due to the actions of the most famous Roman of all. About 170 years before Emperor Hadrian, Julius Caesar abruptly transformed the Roman Republic into an empire. After many successful conquests, he quickly assumed total political power and initiated a series of government reforms, including a new standardized solar calendar that would eventually bear his name. His reign came to a sudden end when he was assassinated five years later, but the Julian calendar would prevail unchallenged for well over 1,500 years.

Even though the Moon had been a convenient way to measure time, it didn't align very well with a solar year. Julius Caesar had witnessed the problem firsthand while conquering various nations all over Europe and Africa. Lunar calendars always came with several leftover days at the end of a year. The Romans had tried by adding a 13th month, but the pattern was determined by full moon and hard to follow. Meanwhile, many astronomers had determined a year was 365 and ¼ days and had proposed an alternate calendar complete with a leap year system. Attempts to combine it with existing lunar calendars had failed all over the ancient world. Julius Caesar's solution was to abandon the Moon's connection to the calendar altogether.

The changes that were needed to implement the Julian calendar were straightforward. The new Roman calendar would still be divided into 12 months, but ten days were added evenly across the year for a new total of 365 days, and a leap day would be added to Februarius (February) every four years. There is a common misconception that the length of February was deliberately shortened by Julius Caesar and his son Augustus to increase the length of July and August, which were renamed in their honor, but this is only a myth. February was simply the last full month of the year before spring began. An extra 13th month had often appeared after February in earlier calendars, so the leap day was added in the same place. Perhaps the most difficult part of adopting the new calendar occurred in 46 B.C., the last year before the reformed calendar took effect. To get his new calendar properly aligned, Julius Caesar decreed an extra two leap months for a year lasting 445 days. This year is often referred to as both the "Longest Year in History" and "The Year of Confusion."

As the Roman Empire fell, the Julian calendar continued its predominance in Europe through the Roman Catholic Church. One of the additional concerns of the Church's solar calendar was calculating the occurrence of its central religious holiday, Easter Sunday. This was a complicated task since Easter was originally defined by the Jewish Passover holiday, which was part of a lunar-based calendar. In the sixth century A.D., the Roman monk Dionysius Exiguus painstakingly calculated a new set of tables for Easter but went one step further. Years were still being counted according to the reign of the current Roman leader. Dionysius Exiguus reasoned a calendar used by Christians should be numbered based on the birth year of Jesus Christ and determined that the current year was 525 A.D. or Anno Domini, which translates as "in the year of the Lord." How he determined the number is not exactly clear, and it's suspected that he might have made a mistake. The Easter tables were later replaced with the Paschal Full Moon system, a theoretical full moon based on mathematical rules designed to calculate Passover in a solar calendar, but Anno Domini was formally adopted along with the early calculations of Dionysius Exiguus. This numbering system is now the global standard.

The Julian calendar would continue uninterrupted until the 1500s, when a curious flaw finally became apparent. The need to synchronize calendars to the seasons had been conveniently eliminated by converting to a solar calendar. Freed from any concern to align with the phases of the Moon, the Julian calendar was a much easier system to use, but its overall simplification had caused a problem. Unlike its predecessors, it had no means of seasonal verification or realignment. Astronomers had been confident that such complications were no longer needed, but the Julian system wasn't nearly as perfect as originally thought. Simple fractions rarely exist in astronomy, and a complete solar year actually falls short of a full 365 and ¼ days by nearly 12 minutes. The difference might seem small, but the cumulative effect caused the Julian calendar to gain a full day approximately every 130 years. Without synchronizing to a winter solstice, the Julian calendar had advanced a full ten days, and religious holidays were no longer correctly aligned to their intended seasons.

The solution, introduced during the time of Roman Pope Gregory XIII, was simple. A leap year would be skipped every century but added back every 400 years, and this basic rule is still used today. For example, with the Gregorian calendar, a leap year was skipped in 1900, but not in 2000. Although the new rule was easy to implement, the more complicated issue of realignment remained. Similar but opposite to the beginning of the Julian Calendar, ten days needed to be eliminated. The Catholic Church did this starting on October 5, 1582. Ten days officially were removed, and the Gregorian calendar officially began.

The conversion to the Gregorian calendar was not immediately accepted throughout the known world. Unlike the Julian calendar, no single empire existed to accelerate the process. Religious and political differences created barriers that would last for centuries. The British Empire and its colonies were notable holdouts and did not accept the change until 1752. This created unique problems in recordkeeping that required the use of dual dating systems. Historical dating from this era can be quite complex, as different countries chose different years and different dates to convert. If the conversion in the United States had occurred just 30 years later than it did, it might have added a considerable amount of confusion to many famous dates in early U.S. history. Fortunately for the history books, that wasn't the case, although there was one minor exception.

George Washington was born on what was then February 11, 1731, according to the old Julian calendar. By that time, a large part of Europe had already converted to the Gregorian calendar, but Great Britain and her colonies had not and were 11 days out of alignment. When the change finally occurred, it triggered the adjustments of many records, including some birth dates. Washington's birthday shifted 11 days to February 22, where it would stay. By 1830, it was being celebrated in many parts of the United States and was eventually phased in as an official federal holiday between 1879 and 1885. The holiday continued to use the adjusted date of February 22, even though technically Washington was born on February 11. This unusual situation became trivial in 1971, when Washington's birthday officially became Presidents' Day, and was observed as the third Monday in February. Ironically, Washington's birthday is now celebrated between February 15 and 21, and completely misses both the Julian and Gregorian birthdates.

Although the solar-based Julian calendar was flawed, the transition to the Gregorian proved to be only a minor footnote in history. The transition further proved that the Moon no longer was needed as part of a calendar system. The misalignment caused by the Julian calendar was more to do with a poor approximation of a solar year. Abandoning the lunar calendar meant abandoning the winter solstice as a means of correction, and just 12 extra unaccounted minutes every year would one day cause George Washington to shift his birthday 11 days. Just as Washington's birthday had become unhinged from its original date, the modern month would lose its original meaning. There was no further direct connection between the Moon and a calendar month. Moon phases still are occasionally found on some calendars, but they haven't aligned to the month for a long time. We track the Moon's phases with calendars and not the other way around. Civilization's need for greater accuracy had surpassed what the Moon could provide.

By the Clock

On June 20, 1837, at precisely 6 o'clock in the morning, Princess Alexandrina Victoria of Kent awoke from her bed to discover that she had become the new Queen of Great Britain and the British Empire. Queen Victoria was barely 18 years old, but she would remain on the throne for over 60 years, mirroring the dominance of the British Empire. In what is sometimes referred to as the Imperial Century, Britain ruled over a quarter of Earth's population and land.

A common patriotic phrase from that time stated that the "Sun would never set on the British Empire," and this proud boast was technically correct. The British Empire covered enough of the globe so that the Sun would always shine on at least part of it. But what was true for the Sun could be said of the Moon as well. Subjects of the British Empire could perpetually watch the Moon, and this would prove extremely influential to global navigation. Definitions of day and night were being replaced by a global 24-hour system as better transportation made the entire world more accessible.

The peculiarities of traveling across the globe during that time inspired the final plot twist in *Around the World in 80 Days*, written by Jules Verne in 1872. When hero Phileas Fogg returns to England, he believes he has failed to complete his journey in 80 days until he discovers he has gained an extra day by traveling the globe in an easterly direction. Traveling against the rotation of Earth has shortened his days by four minutes for every longitude he's crossed. While Fogg has seen 80 sunrises during his journey, London has only seen 79.

Gaining or losing a day by crossing the international dateline is a common fact of global travel today, but it was a novel concept in the 1800s.

Schedules and timetables allowed Fogg to travel around the world, but an understanding of global time ultimately saves the day. Fogg's need for precision became the standard behavior for the British Empire.

Britain's global power was heavily based on control of the sea with a formidable navy and a large fleet of merchant ships. Precise navigation at sea heavily depended on the accurate measurement of time. By comparing the local time on a ship to the known time at a specific location, a skilled navigator could calculate the distance between those two points and determine the longitudinal (east or west) position of his ship. This required a common reference point known as a prime meridian, commonly known today as zero degrees longitude. Various prime meridians existed in the early 1800s, with different nations favoring their own, but Britain had taken an early competitive lead by naming the Royal Observatory at Greenwich as its prime meridian in 1751.

As part of its service to navigation, the Greenwich Observatory promoted the lunar method for navigating at sea. Without the lunar method, knowing the time at the prime meridian required a special sea clock that was preset to Greenwich Time before leaving harbor. Keeping a typical mechanical clock accurate on the rolling seas was nearly impossible, and the newly invented sea clocks were rare and expensive. Although laborious and less accurate than a sea clock, using the Moon to navigate was a practical alternative. The idea behind the lunar method was simple. The Moon could be thought of as the giant hour hand of a clock. Its position in the night sky was predictable and could be calculated in advance. By comparing the position of the Moon to known stars and consulting pre-computed tables, a navigator could deduce what time it was back in Greenwich, England, without the need for a special clock.

The lunar method tables naturally were calculated using Greenwich as a prime meridian which, among other reasons, led to Greenwich becoming a popular universal choice for navigators worldwide. A survey conducted in 1879 suggested that Greenwich was being used by nearly two-thirds of all the world's ships as their prime meridian, so an international conference made it official in 1884. Greenwich became zero degrees of longitude. Greenwich Mean Time had already been adopted as the official time for of all Great Britain several years earlier due to the need to unify British railway schedules. Other time zones quickly were established around the world, especially in countries with existing train service, and all were aligned to Greenwich Time.

Since its empire spanned the entire world, consistent high-speed communication was just as critical as precise navigation. To solve this problem, Britain took advantage of the newly created telegraph technology and monopolized the industry, placing it decades ahead of any other country. By 1876, most of the empire was linked into a single real-time network known collectively as the All Red Line. For the first time in history, it was possible to send instantaneous messages around the world. From a central point of London, Great Britain could synchronize its entire empire to a single unified clock.

Originally known as simply the Clock Tower, Big Ben was completed in 1865 with much fanfare and celebration. Nicknamed after its massive, 13-ton bell, it would become the world's most famous clock and still tells the time at the heart of a city, country, and culture obsessed with the accuracy of time and the glory of fine precision. Rightly considered a crowning achievement of Victorian technology and mechanical clocks, it also represents the end of an era. Tourists and London residents whose mobile phones are even more accurate now surround it.

The earliest mechanical clock still running is the Prague astronomy clock. First installed in 1410, it reveals an important shift in cultural priorities. While not originally as accurate as Big Ben, it displays an equally impressive array of astronomical data, including the phases of the Moon. The differences between the two clocks illustrate time becoming a simplified abstraction. The Moon was no longer an integral part of time. Much like Big Ben, it symbolized an older way to measure time that had since been surpassed. The Moon's once unarguable contribution to society was slowly slipping away.

The Dawn of Time

On July 20, 1969, at exactly 02:56:15 UTC (10:56:15 p.m. Eastern Standard Time), Neil Armstrong stepped off the lunar lander, and humanity made physical contact with the Moon for the very first time. We had come full circle from looking at it to walking on it. Just as with the huge jump forward in time seen in *2001: A Space Odyssey*, we had completed a greater journey through time as our civilization grew. Learning how to measure time more precisely is an often-overlooked key component of that journey. The Moon was our original guide to marking out the days. It gave us our first calendars, but we eventually grew beyond its precision.

Two thousand years before humans walked on the Moon, lunar calendars were being phased out in favor of a better system, but our drive for better time measurement didn't end there. Sundials were replaced with mechanical clocks that gradually improved over time until accuracy was within a fraction of a second per day. By the time Neil Armstrong walked on the Moon, our ability to define time was so precise that it surpassed using Earth as a guide. In 1967, just two years before landing on the Moon, a day was officially redefined to be equal to 86,400 seconds marked off by an atomic clock. A day was determined by the length of a second and not the other way around. The connection to Earth's rotation was broken. Neil Armstrong's footprint is symbolic of a new age, but it also marks a new way to measure time.

The modern epoch of time began the following year in 1970, although its effect was only known to a few. The task of measuring the passage of time was given to computers that counted out the seconds with a precision we couldn't attain. Every event of a computer's day is recorded with a timestamp of the total number of seconds since the beginning of January 1, 1970. This moment marks the time of transition, usually referred to as Epoch time. The public didn't really notice the switch to computers, which makes it reminiscent of sinister science-fiction plots of the same era. Computers did not take over the world in the 1970s, but several related technologies became world standards. A prototype of the Internet, called ARPANET, officially began in 1969, and the standard operating system called UNIX started a few years later. Global computer systems required a unified clock system with a single coordinated starting point, and the beginning of the decade seemed a reasonable choice. UNIX quickly grew to become the predominant operating system and set a precedent for future systems, including personal computers and smartphones.

Fictional cybernetic beings from the future might look back to January 1, 1970, as the dawn of digital time. If they did, they might consider their Father Time to be Louis Essen, the inventor of the atomic clock and digital time. Essen was an English physicist who worked at the National Physics Laboratory in Great Britain for most of his career. His early work toward digital time focused first on quartz technology. This would lead to electric clocks with an improved accuracy of one second in four months. Essen's transition to atomic clocks began in 1950 with a visit to the United States. While there, he learned of a failed attempt to produce an atomic clock and felt that he could solve the problem using some of his own ideas.

Essen's plan was to use cesium-133 as its atomic structure gave him easy access to the transition state of a single electron. This idea proved to be the right approach, and his first prototype clock had an accuracy of one second in every 300 years. The original production atomic clock started ticking in 1955 with an astounding accuracy of one second every 1.4 million years, but Essen's work on time didn't end there. He used research gained from his atomic clock to propose a new standard definition of time. A cesium second was the transition frequency of a cesium-133 atom multiplied 9,192,631,770 times. The International Standards Committee adopted Essen's proposal in 1967.

We could no longer use astronomy to tell time. At a microscopic level, Earth's rotational speed was random and gradually slowing down. Astronomy and science required a greater precision than Earth could provide. The job of keeping the most accurate time in the world transferred from Greenwich Observatory to the National Physics Laboratory and eventually a series of atomic clocks around the world. Greenwich Mean Time was phased out and replaced with Universal Time Coordinated, or UTC, between 1967 and 1972. Any discrepancies with Earth's rotation are resolved with the occasional leap second, where the UTC is pushed back to match a slightly slowing Earth. As of this writing, there have been 27 leap seconds added to international clocks to keep Universal Time in line with Earth's slowing rotation.

As a timekeeper, Earth eventually proved to be as much of a relic as the Moon. Going to the Moon required digital precision where every stage was timed to the second. The Space Age required the precision of an atomic clock, and it signaled the beginning of a final paradigm shift for humanity. The Moon no longer times us. We time the Moon, and we have discovered that the Moon and Earth are slowly changing. Patterns in sandstone rock show that 620 million years ago, a day lasted 21.9 hours. The major cause of the slowdown is the Moon's tidal effect, which acts like a braking mechanism for Earth. This same mechanism is also pushing the Moon away from us by a slight but measurable amount each year. Retroreflectors left on the Moon by Apollo missions allow us to bounce a laser light off the surface and measure the distance to the Moon to a fraction of a centimeter.

Every year, the Moon's orbit extends out by another three centimeters. It will take millions of years to leave, but the eternal Moon is not eternal after all. As it slowly drifts away from Earth, we have symbolically tossed it out as much as we can. As a sentinel of the past, the Moon's remaining legacy is tied to our calendar, which seems grossly out of step with digital clocks. There have been proposals to change the calendar to a digital system for centuries. Perhaps, if our civilization also leaves Earth, it will make sense to create a new calendar. For now, we will be Moon-Watchers of a different kind.

Moon Secret 6: There are seas on the Moon.

The dark areas on the Moon are leftovers from a volcanic past. Although inactive today, the Moon once leaked magma into giant pools of volcanic seas. The magma cooled, leaving a darker colored rock than the rest of the surface due to heavy iron content. The areas were first cataloged by the Italian astronomer Giovanni Riccioli in the late 1600s, who called them oceans, seas, and lakes because that's what they appeared to be. They are still known today as the Mare, or the Seas of the Moon. Apollo 11 landed near the edge of the Sea of Tranquility, and Neil Armstrong referred to the landing site as Tranquility Base.

Dusk in Autumn

The moon is like a scimitar
A little silver scimitar,
A-drifting down the sky.
And near beside it is a star

SARA TEASDALE

MAY:
The Mystic Warrior

The Milk Moon (Colonial American)

(The secret battle between the Sun and the Moon)

The Case of the Mysterious Duel

S herlock Holmes had little interest in the Moon or astronomy, or so he claimed. In A *Study in Scarlet*, Arthur Conan Doyle's earliest work printed in 1887, he declares to Dr. Watson upon their introduction that even a basic knowledge of the Solar System was a waste of his time:

> "...you say that we go round the sun. If we went round the moon it would not make a pennyworth of difference to me or to my work."

This was possibly a ruse on Holmes's part to prove a point about his method. References to the Moon and astronomy would regularly appear in the adventures of Sherlock Holmes, but they were never crucial in solving a case. In reality, the Moon is linked to one of the greatest scientific mysteries of all time, and solving it would lead to a surprising revelation. As Sherlock gained fame for solving crimes in the late 19th century, astronomers were making headway in solving a baffling case of their own. It would eventually expand into a case of theft and attempted murder, but it would take over a hundred years to put all the pieces together.

The most obvious clues to the great mystery can be found in the night sky by anyone who's in the right place. For those who live in the far north and south, the aurora borealis and aurora australis offer a rare visual feast that seems to outdo the more ordinary Moon. Twirling across the sky in bold waves of color, they seem totally unrelated to the slow-moving monochromatic Moon, but there is a secret bond that protects our world.

To the Aboriginal Australians, auroras were fires from the spirit world, either as a display of evil spirits called the Kootchee, or messages from long departed ancestors. A 19th century reinterpretation of Norse mythology attributes the lights to the magical glow of swords and armor of the Valkyrie, legendary female warriors battling evil, but this is a modern myth as the aurora was never mentioned in Norse literature.

In 1619, Galileo mistakenly thought them to be the first light of morning. As a result, he named them after the Roman goddess of the morning and the Greek word for a northern wind. Like the Moon, a clear understanding of the auroras has eluded science until the 20th century. Now freed of their mystic context, auroras embody a truly epic struggle between the magnetic forces of the Sun and Earth.

The Sun's deadly weapon in this battle is a constant stream of charged particles known as the solar wind. Usually invisible to the naked eye, we see it best with the shaping of a comet's tail. It constantly shoots past Earth at supersonic speeds and continues well beyond the boundaries of the solar system. Earth's only defense against the onslaught is its own powerful magnetic field, which pushes the solar wind back and forces it to go around. The real battle in the night sky rages constantly but is fought in outer space at an atomic level. Earth has held its ground for millions of years with the aid of a surprising ally that until recently has remained anonymous.

Clues to the mystery of Earth's defense were in plain sight, but it took time to understand them. First came the secrets of the auroras and Earth's magnetic field that drives them. Beyond their beguiling beauty, the auroras are an important sign that Earth is protected from the harmful effects of the Sun. This includes shielding to protect Earth's atmosphere. Without a magnetic field, the Sun's steady assault would slowly steal away our atmosphere. Unprotected oxygen and nitrogen atoms would bind to charged particles from the Sun and permanently be pulled out into space. Although it would take millions of years, the damage would be irreversible and eventually leave Earth with no breathable air. All life would die.

From a satellite view, it is easy to visualize the magnetic field doing its job, as the auroras often look like two gigantic glowing rings surrounding each of Earth's magnetic poles. From the ground, parts of these circles appear as giant tubes or walls of swirling color. The glow is now known to be caused by a series of electrical interactions with different colors produced by different interactions. Specifically, the eerie hallmark luminescent green results from a charging of oxygen atoms at high altitudes. The flowing wave motion is not caused by wind, as Galileo thought, but by ever-fluctuating changes within Earth's magnetic field. When the fluid-like nature of the auroras was connected back to the magnetic field, their secrets were unlocked, and their hidden accomplice was revealed.

Far away, the Moon appears an unassuming witness. With no life or breathable atmosphere, its influence seems limited to gravity. The Moon has no volcanic activity and a barely detectable magnetic field. Its inner core has cooled millions of years ago, leaving it with no energy to power a stronger one. Without a protective shield, the Moon's atmosphere has been blown away into space long ago. It is a dead world, and yet it supports life on Earth unexpectedly. In 2013, a team of French scientists determined that the Moon is constantly adding energy to Earth's magnetic field through gravity. The strength of Earth's magnetic field depends on Earth's staying hot, but mathematical models have suggested that Earth should be a lot cooler than it is. How was Earth able to maintain a higher temperature than expected? Unbeknownst to us, the Moon's gravity was the culprit all along. The mystery of the auroras reveals a rare connection between gravity and magnetism that keeps life safe.

Above and Below

A t the center of Earth, there is a solid core of iron and nickel that's nearly as big as the Moon. Except for this peculiar similarity, the Moon and the inner core share little in common, but the two spheres work together to build a magnetic field that protects all life.

Jules Verne, who knew nothing about the core, wrote *Journey to the Center of the Earth* only a year before his voyage From the Earth to the Moon. As fictional journeys, both were equally possible, but unlike the Moon, Earth's fiery core never will be conquered by heroic adventurers. With temperatures hotter than the surface of the Sun and pressures millions of times stronger than that at sea level, Earth's center never will be visited or even seen by humans. The deepest penetration to the center of Earth ended in 1979 at only slightly longer than 7.5 miles when the surrounding rock became too hot to continue. Going beyond this record will be a struggle, and it is a tiny fraction of the 3,100 miles needed to reach the inner core or the 240,000 miles to reach the Moon.

Isaac Newton could use the Moon to define gravity, but he had no such assistance when it came to Earth's magnetism. He even proclaimed it "the great remaining unsolved mystery," and unlocking Earth's well-kept secret became a scientific obsession in the 19th century. The British Navy was especially interested in using it to improve navigation. With massive fleets of huge ships, navigational errors had caused disastrous accidents. Using a compass on the open sea was not new. They had been used on ships in both China and Europe for hundreds of years, but there were issues of consistency. There were natural deviations all over the world. A compass wouldn't always point to due North. Astronomer

Edmund Halley had suggested that the deviations could be used as a part of a navigational guide if they could be properly charted, but this idea turned out to be fruitless. There was too much local variation in Earth's magnetic field, and the entire magnetic field was also slowly changing.

Historical data shows that Earth's magnetic North Pole has been moving across the Canadian Arctic since at least 1590. Its position was first clearly identified to be in the Abernethy Bay of northern Canada in 1831, but further expeditions repeatedly found the North Pole to be in different locations. By 1946, the United States and Canada had separately established that the pole had shifted some 250 miles north by northwest from its 1831 location. Since that time, the magnetic North Pole has been tracked to be moving north and passed near the geographic North Pole in the year 2020.

The mysteriously shifting magnetic North Pole was part of a misconception about how Earth's magnetism worked. It's easy to assume that if Earth acts like a gigantic magnet, it would also be constructed like one. Since magnets commonly are hard rigid metal, it would follow that Earth would be as well, but Earth's magnetic field is driven by a combination of a solid inner core and liquid outer core known as a geodynamo. Earth's inner core releases energy as heat to the outer core, which causes convection currents like a bubbling pot of water. The outer core is a hot, liquid combination of iron and nickel. This fluidity explains why Earth's North and South Poles aren't perfectly aligned and drift independently. The randomness is also seen in the massive wavy lines of magnetic force that wrap around Earth like a giant fingerprint.

The idea of at least a partial liquid core isn't that hard to accept, as evidenced by volcanoes spewing liquid magma to Earth's surface, but details on the inner workings of the core weren't understood until the 20th century. A hollow Earth was even considered a likely possibility, and Edmund Halley and John Quincy Adams were two notable proponents of the idea. Charles Hutton proved it false in 1774, when he successfully measured the density of Earth and showed it to be solid. Still the notion persisted, and Adams even proposed an expedition to the poles, where a potential entrance could be found. The journey never occurred. The details of discovery were left to fiction writers like Jules Verne. Scientists finally gained entry of sorts by listening to Earth, with the messages coming in the form of earthquakes.

Seismographs had been capturing data or earthquake waves since the late 1800s. This would eventually lead to a field of study in the 20th century. It was discovered that when earthquakes occur, they create several distinct wave patterns that travel through Earth differently. This was first identified by pioneer female seismologist Inge Lehmann in 1936. A main source of her study was the massive 7.3 Murchison earthquake that struck New Zealand in 1929. From that data, she was the first to identify P Wave arrivals as they traveled around Earth's core. During an earthquake, a P Wave is a compression wave that travels through the ground faster than the more destructive S Wave. Sometimes, it can act as an effective earthquake warning. While studying P Waves, Lehmann noted a P Wave shadow, an area within Earth where P Waves bounced back. Based on the data, she deduced Earth had an inner solid core that was surrounded by an outer liquid layer. Her interpretation was so incontrovertible it was quickly accepted by other leading seismologists within a few years. It was a major accomplishment in an era notably biased against women scientists.

Earth has been slow to give up all its secrets. Even today, there are many details about Earth's core and its magnetic field that are not fully understood. Paleomagnetism, which studies the magnetic field through history, suggests the core and the magnetic field formed approximately two to three billion years ago, with the field becoming much stronger about one to one and a half billion years ago. Based on such data, computer models have predicted that Earth's core should have cooled a lot more than it has, but the Moon's effect on Earth had not been considered until recently. The Moon acts like a giant crank shaft, not unlike the earliest generator created by Michael Faraday in 1831. It is estimated that 3,700 billion watts of power are constantly being transferred into Earth every day, mostly by the gravitational forces of the Moon. One thousand billion watts of this energy are then transferred into Earth's inner core. This power boost between the Moon above and the core below stretches the lifespan of Earth's magnetic field. Without the Moon, Earth's core would have cooled, and the magnetic field would have died off long ago.

Ex Luna Scientia

With the success of Apollo 11 officially in the history books, the remaining missions could take more time to focus on lunar research. The launch of Apollo 12, which had been considered a potential backup mission, was pushed back two months to allow for extra training. Subsequent crews would have a better opportunity to deploy more extensive scientific equipment. Each landing team would deploy a collection of self-powered instruments capable of operating after the astronauts had left. Their work would lead to important clues about the Moon's inner core and its connection to Earth. Known as the ALSEP for short, the Apollo Lunar Surface Experiments Package varied from mission to mission, but most included a passive seismic experiment for studying moonquakes.

The crew of Apollo 13 had intended to continue the scientific research of previous missions but is regrettably remembered for a missed opportunity to land on the Moon. Their motto of "Ex Luna Scientia," or "from the Moon, knowledge," could have summed up the entire Apollo program, but the mission objective shifted from discovery to survival. Crippled by an oxygen tank explosion, they were forced to settle for a mere flyby of the Moon. Even this small consolation proved to be significant as the modified course and the Moon's position combined to set a distance record. As their lifeless spacecraft swung around the Moon, they officially traveled farther from Earth than any other humans during the Apollo era.

The study of the Fra Mauro crater would be handed off to Apollo 14, but Apollo 13 still contributed to the study of the Moon in an unexpected way by using their spent third-stage rocket booster. Like the other third stages, it was used to break out of Earth's orbit. After separation, it continued traveling toward the Moon and arrived on a similar trajectory. Mission control deliberately crashed it on the surface of the Moon to calibrate seismograph instruments left behind by Apollo 12. It was the first Apollo third stage to be used in this way.

NASA added similar equipment on later missions, creating a small network of moonquake detectors, and would slam all remaining third-stage rockets onto the Moon's surface. The resulting moonquakes allowed scientists to create a valuable picture of the Moon's inner core just as earthquakes had done for Earth. With improved measurements of the locations of the crash sites coming from NASA's LRO, the data continues to reveal a better picture of the Moon's interior. The Moon contains both an inner solid iron core and outer liquid one. Moon rocks proved the Moon once had a magnetic field 3 billion years ago, and recent studies of those rocks indicate that it may have lasted longer than suspected with high amounts of sulfur in the core allowing the heat transfer to continue. The Moon has had a complex past and geology could re-create it much like it has done on Earth.

Man-made moonquakes were not the only ones detected by the Apollo seismic stations. NASA discovered regularly occurring natural moonquakes as well. This was a surprise since, geologically, the Moon was thought to be a dead world. The quakes eventually were broken down into categories, complete with corresponding explanations. The deeper quakes were results of tidal stress commonly seen as the Moon reaches its perihelion, or maximum distance in orbit. Quakes closer to the surface were determined to be either meteor impacts, or the result of a quick expansion brought on by temperature shifts. The remaining 28 shallow quakes observed were not as easily explained. They once were considered evidence of limited tectonic activity on the Moon, but the prevailing theory is that the slowly shrinking Moon causes them. Since its core has cooled, the outward pressure of expanding heat has diminished, leaving the Moon free to collapse under its own weight.

When the Apollo 13 crew heard that the third stage had successfully impacted the Moon, command module pilot Jack Swigert exclaimed:

"Well, at least something worked on this flight."

Swigert probably felt the greatest amount of frustration and doubt. The explosion happened when he attempted to routinely stir the oxygen tanks. After the mission, NASA had a different kind of mystery to solve. It was eventually discovered that two unrelated events combined to turn the service module's Number 2 tank into a bomb. Five years before the mission, all of Apollo's electrical systems were upgraded to handle higher voltage. Notification of this change was never passed on to the tank's thermostat manufacturer. This defect was not critical on its own, but a small air tube on Number 2 tank had been damaged during a minor accident. Undetected during safety checks, the damaged tube would later prevent ground crews from easily draining the tank after a preflight test. To encourage the oxygen to drain, the tank was heated, but high voltage from ground power welded its thermostats shut. As a result, the temperatures got too hot, and the intense heat melted the electrical insulation and exposed bare wires. When Swigert flipped the switch, a spark ignited the oxygen. The tank exploded and ripped the service module apart. Oxygen was not only critical for breathing, but also used to charge the three command module batteries. Within minutes, Apollo 13 was out of power.

The Moon swings around our planet as a drained battery, and yet that motion helps keep Earth charged. The lifeless Moon is the unsung hero of Earth's ecosystem. When life finally came to the Moon in the form of astronauts, we explored the Moon's core in the same way we had explored Earth's core. The motto of Apollo 13 was fulfilled after all, and the ill-fated mission unexpectedly summarized the Moon's distant past. Lacking power to sustain its magnetic field, the Moon's atmosphere drained into space long ago. The remaining desolate surface serves as a reminder of how critical a magnetic field is to all life.

A Study in Rock

S herlock Holmes can be found on the Moon in the form of a crater. Many craters around the Apollo landing sites were named by the astronauts to help them navigate the Moon. Too small to be seen from Earth, they were photographed by the Lunar Orbiter probes as part of Apollo's preparatory phase. As he was the only astronaut trained in geology, Harrison Schmitt played an important role in selecting the Apollo landing sites, and he also named most of the craters for the Apollo 17 mission. His choices for names were based on real and fictional people that had a personal significance. In the case of Sherlock Holmes, Schmitt later wrote:

> "Sherlock Holmes, whose adventures were preserved for us by Dr. Watson, was not only the world's most famous and most brilliant detective, but was also one of the leading geological thinkers of his time. His knowledge of London soils and many other aspects of nature, combined with his use of deductive reasoning, serve as examples to all who aspire to understand the worlds around us."

In the spirit of Sherlock Holmes, geologists apply deductive reasoning to both the Moon and the Earth. Their shared history gives lunar geology a subtle double meaning. The word "geology" originally meant the study of Earth's history, but lunar geology also refers to moon rocks that were once a part of Earth. Mysteries found on the Moon's surface can solve related questions back on Earth and vice versa. Similar techniques often produce similar results, and this has uncovered unexpected connections between volcanism, magnetism and even gravity.

Scientific measurements of Earth's magnetic field only date back to 1840, so studying beyond that requires other methods. While not as precise, useful data about Earth's magnetic field in the distant past can be pulled from magnetic rocks. When iron-based rocks are molten, their magnetic properties are in flux. Once they cool, the iron components in the rock align to Earth's magnetic field, and their polarity and magnetic strength is permanently recorded. Japanese geophysicist Motonori Matuyama first discovered this in 1920, when he noticed that all rocks from the early Pleistocene Age or earlier suggested a magnetic field reversal. This technique recently has been applied to moon rocks to reveal details of the Moon's magnetic past.

In the 1950s, deep-sea mapping of the ocean floor revealed a repeated pattern of magnetic field reversals. These patterns provided concrete evidence of continental drift. As the sea floor slowly expanded due to volcanic activity, Earth's changing magnetic field would polarize new volcanic layers. When the field flipped, the polarity was sealed in the magma as it cools. This discovery allowed for the dating of field reversals, resulting in a complete history going back millions of years. Magnetic field reversals have made a regular splash in the media ever since their discovery. Some suggest that since the average time between polarity shifts is 450,000 years, and the last reversal occurred 780,000 years ago, Earth is due for a magnetic flip. Such Doomsday headlines naturally get a lot of attention. However, there's no statistical proof to indicate that changes occur at regular intervals. Just like early volcanism that gradually tapered off, Earth's current magnetic field is experiencing an extremely long stable period.

To discover more recent and detailed data on Earth's magnetic field, scientists have applied a similar technique to ancient pottery. Clay pots contain iron ore, and when the clay pot is baked in the oven, Earth's current polarity and the strength of Earth's magnetic field is permanently recorded in the clay. By studying a series of clay pots created throughout human history, a complete record of Earth's magnetic field is created. The results show that the field strength can vary, even over just a few thousand years. Although its strength has been steadily diminishing in recent times, there was a huge spike in 8000 B.C., when it was double what it is today. Regular fluctuations in Earth's magnetic field might be the norm.

The approach of studying baked ore to discover locked data about magnetic fields recently has been applied to the Moon as well. Samples of moon rocks have been heated to discover a more precise history of the Moon's magnetic field. The Moon once had a much stronger magnetic field than was commonly thought, and Earth was likely a contributing factor. Four billion years ago, the Moon was a lot closer to Earth and had a field at least twice as strong as what Earth has today. The proximity to Earth caused a liquid dynamo reaction in the Moon's core, producing a strong magnetic field. The Moon would have been protected from the solar wind just like Earth, but as the Moon drifted away the core changed. Earth's tidal effect on the Moon weakened, and the Moon's core solidified. Initially, the solidification process could have also generated a magnetic field, but the result was not permanent. The Moon's magnetic field permanently faded away around one to one and a half billion years ago.

On their final EVA, Harrison Schmitt and Gene Cernan drove past the crater named after Sherlock Holmes. It was a symbolic reminder that Apollo astronauts had brought deductive reasoning to the Moon, and geologists would later apply the same process to the rocks they brought back. This has since given us an insight into a key difference between the Moon and Earth. The Moon lost its magnetic field when it drifted too far away from Earth, but its unique size and proximity still play a pivotal role in Earth's magnetic field.

The Moon Electric

The essential clue to the Moon's connection to Earth's magnetic field began with a totally unrelated discovery. In 1843, German astronomer Heinrich Schwabe noticed a curious pattern in the frequency of sunspots seen on the Sun. It would be the first in a line of discoveries that would unravel the mysteries of the Sun and Earth, and eventually the Moon as well. Sunspots are small areas of the Sun's surface that appear darker than the surrounding area. They were often mistaken for planets by earlier astronomers, so Schwabe meticulously tracked them every clear day for 17 years while he searched for a possible new inner planet. What Schwabe discovered instead was an eleven-year cycle where the number of sunspots would peak and then diminish. Swiss astronomer Rudolph Wolf continued Schwabe's work and established a solar cycle numbering system in 1848 that is still in use today, but neither Schwabe nor Wolf had a good explanation why sunspot cycles occurred so regularly.

The peak of the next solar cycle was dramatically marked with the Great Solar Storm of 1859. Of interest to detective novel fans, the year also saw the birth of Sir Arthur Conan Doyle, the creator of the greatest detective of all. The year would also lead to a lucky break in the science of Earth's magnetism. During the night of September 1, the skies around the world were bathed in some of the brightest auroras ever recorded. They were reportedly bright enough to read by in New England and seen as far south as Hawaii and Mexico. The amazing light show was followed the next day by a bizarre outage of telegraph lines. While most were overloaded, a few mysteriously continued to work with no power.

The opportunity to find a connection between these two consecutive events might have been missed if it wasn't for the well-timed observations of English astronomer Richard Carrington. Around noon on the previous day, he made history when he recorded the first solar flare as it erupted from the surface of the Sun. Later, it was realized that the solar flare was responsible for both the super brilliant aurora and the telegraph failures as it bombarded Earth's magnetic field with tremendous energy. The solar flare, which remains the most powerful ever recorded, was also perfectly timed for our civilization. Its impact was minimal and limited to service disruptions of the newly developed telegraph, but the advancement of knowledge in geomagnetism and astrophysics was considerable. The solution to the mystery of auroras would eventually follow.

Today, the shielding effect of Earth's magnetic field is well understood, but the Moon's place in the continuing battle only came from recent discoveries. Since the time of Newton, the Moon's predominant effect on Earth was gravity, but Schwabe's early work on sunspots would lead to an unexpected revelation. Recently, a German team led by physicist Frank Stefani matched the 11-year cycle to the alignment in the orbits of Jupiter, Earth, and Venus. The combined gravitational effect of these three planets is tiny, but it's enough to cause an instability in the Sun's magnetic field, resulting in increased solar flare activity. This discovery is a unique example of planetary conjunctions having a direct effect on Earth. It oddly supports the basic premise of astrology in an unusual way but should not be confused as proof. Instead, it illustrates how gravity can affect magnetism, and specifically how the Moon's gravity can contribute to Earth's magnetic field.

Tidal heating can be seen elsewhere in the solar system. Jupiter's innermost moon, Io, is subject to the effect from a combined interaction of Jupiter and another moon, Europa. In simplest terms, gravitational forces act as a braking mechanism and transfers the energy of motion into heat. The result has given Io a hot inner core and created approximately 400 volcanoes, making it more volcanically active than Earth. The Moon's effect on Earth is similar but more subtle. Its gravity is slowing down the rotation of Earth and that braking energy is being transferred to Earth's inner core.

The great mystery of the 19th century has been solved. Thanks in part to the Moon, Earth's core temperature has cooled very little, and the strength of its geodynamo-based energy remains steady. This in turn powers Earth's magnetic field and forces harmful solar winds to travel around the planet. Life flourishes while mostly oblivious to the great battle in the sky, but the Moon's contribution to that battle is finally appreciated. On a cold night in the North, the aurora is a reassuring sign that Earth's core is being kept warm by the Moon, and that energy provides extra protection for life on the planet. On rare nights when both the Moon and aurora are visible, knowing that one is indirectly affecting the other turns a feeling of mystery into one of wonder.

PART 3:

SUMMER
Believing in the Moon

The Moon holds a special meaning beyond pure science. It is the crossroads of opposing schools of thought. Ancient beliefs remain embedded in the Moon despite it being an object of science.

June: Looking for a Sign
July: Real Lunacy
August: The Leap of Faith

Moon Secret 7: The Moon rules the United States.

Astrologers traditionally use the signing of the Declaration of Independence to mark the beginning of the United States. This places it under the sign of Cancer the Crab with the Moon as its ruling celestial object. The Apollo program can be interpreted as a realization of an astrological destiny

A Prophecy: To George Keats in America

'Tis the "witching time of night" –
Orbed is the moon and bright,
And the Stars they glisten, glisten,
Seeming with bright eyes to listen.

JOHN KEATS

JUNE:
Looking for a Sign

The Oak Moon (Southern Hemisphere)

(The Moon foretells of a harmonious destiny)

Lunar Navigation

The night sky fills us with a sense of mystery. Its darkness, the very essence of the unknown, stirs our most foreboding feelings of death and the future. We stare out at the blackness, looking up for answers, while it stares right back and instills us with both intrigue and dread. Within the dark void, stars attempt to fill the gap with little bits of light, beckoning us to discover their purpose. They offer us clues in the patterns that they form and hint at a greater solution, one that connects them—and us—to other mysteries of life. The night sky is a shroud of the unknown, and within it awaits something more profound. The enigma of the stars is to decode their hidden mystery.

The Moon along with the stars holds a place in two worldviews that are incompatible. Astrologically, its position predicts favorable opportunities related to our changing emotions, but it's also part of verified facts that refute the legitimacy of astrology. This is not a new position for the Moon. The two views originally lived in harmony. Ancient astronomers from Sumeria, India, and the Arab world recorded scientific measurements alongside astrological conjectures about what it all meant, but the world of science grew. Technology transformed the Moon, but the astrological part remained frozen in time. It is a remnant of an older mode of thinking that we are not totally ready to abandon.

Our metaphysical trust in the stars likely is derived from solving more earthly problems. If they could aid in determining real-world orientations, then perhaps they could also assist in more esoteric matters. Stars have helped humans navigate the seas for thousands of years and even guided astronauts toward the Moon. Geolocation satellites have made star navigation mostly obsolete today, but it was a critical issue during the development of the Apollo program. Command module pilot Jim Lovell of Apollo 8 became the first navigator to use stars in outer space. As a former navy pilot, his adept mastery of such an ancient skill would prove fortuitous for the mission.

For centuries, the position of Deneb on the horizon allowed Polynesian explorers to determine latitude to find the desired trade winds. Polaris would point European sailors to due North when compasses were unreliable or unavailable. Star navigation improved immensely with the introduction of the sextant in the 1700s that allowed the observer to precisely calculate the angle between two points in the night sky. It remained an essential tool of navigators for hundreds of years and was modified for aeronautical usage in the 1920s. Because loss of communication was a real possibility during an Apollo mission, astronauts would need to navigate like the wayfinders of old. The command capsule was equipped with its own navigation computer, telescope, and sextant. The orientation of the spacecraft could be verified by locating any of 35 easily identifiable stars and entering its position into the computer.

The same system also was capable of course corrections which proved invaluable during Apollo 8's return trip to Earth. While running new test navigation programs, Lovell mistakenly entered the wrong command. This triggered the navigation computer to reset the ship's orientation to the beginning of the mission. Not only was the spacecraft aimed in the wrong direction, but the correct orientation had been overwritten. Although this was a critical error, the situation was not lost. Using the ship's sextant to sight the stars Rigel and Sirius, Lovell could realign the ship in about 10 minutes.

Knowledge of the stars saved the crew, but guidance was strictly limited to physical navigation. In space, the principles of astrology did not apply. As Apollo 8 left Earth orbit, the Moon and the Sun positions became mostly fixed. Even stranger, the Moon would spin rapidly through all astrological signs while the spacecraft was orbiting around it. Angles between the Moon and astrological signs lost their significance, and there was no specialty of astronaut astrology to account for this problem. Astrology was created before the true nature of the solar system was understood. As we navigate beyond Earth, how will astrology guide future generations? With that in mind, have the Moon and stars ever guided us in the first place?

Sisterhood of the Moon

A mystic Moon-woman bond is an enduring theme in our culture. Originally personified by female Moon deities, it is a metaphor of the complexities and intrigue associated with human sexuality. We glamorize its mysterious nature and liken it to the equally perplexing mysteries of love. The Moon's ethereal charm has also been claimed as a symbol of female unity and gender empowerment. Its misunderstood influence represents women's unique and often unrecognized contribution to society.

Like many classic themes, the bond has inspired additional meanings, but the basis for this link is an almost practical observation. There is a near identical duration between a full moon cycle and a woman's period. This similarity still occasionally is offered as proof of a hidden connection between humanity and the universe and is possibly the origin for all astrology.

Female kinship with the Moon is an idea that transcends most cultures and magnifies the mystique of both. The Moon phases are a strong affirmation of a fundamental part of womanhood. While much has been made of this unusual coincidence of nature, the overall scientific consensus is that the beauty lies in the coincidence alone. Much as we want to find evidence of an amazing connection, there really isn't one. Lack of support for scientific confirmation hasn't stopped the belief. On the contrary, it is viewed by some as a failure of science to tap into a world it doesn't understand. This leads to a situation of selective reasoning winning out over scientific rationale.

The most often cited work for the Moon's astrological influence over fertility comes from Dr. Eugen Jonas during the 1950s. His intended goal was to devise a natural way to maximize fertility by increasing the chances of conception for women who wanted to have children. While researching ancient writings, he discovered a translation of a Babylonian text that specifically said, "A woman is fertile according to the Moon." From that point, Jonas was inspired to develop an elaborate astrological system that included everything from determining a baby's gender to minimizing birth defects. The core concept was simple. The position of the Moon at a woman's birth would later determine her fertility cycle. In addition, her best chance of conception would occur during a phase of the Moon that matched the one at her birth.

Such sublimely beautiful connections to the cosmos are easy to accept. We desire simple profound truths, but appearing perfectly reasonable doesn't mean they are true. The basic concept of Moon fertility has many flaws that are hard to reconcile, starting with a more precise astronomical and biological comparison. A full lunar cycle as seen from Earth is slightly longer than 29.5 days and never varies, while the average human menstrual cycle is only 28 days and varies from woman to woman and month to month. There is never a precise alignment between the two, only a rough approximation, but the loose association is good enough for proponents of a lunar menstrual synchronization. Any observed irregularities are viewed as adverse factors of women's health, while a solid match to the Moon's phases indicate good health and high chances of conception.

There have been other studies conducted to find patterns in fertility cycles in humans, none of which yielded any convincing evidence. In 1971, Martha McClintock published a study on menstrual synchrony where the onset of women's menstrual cycles fell within four days of each other if they lived together for more than three months. McClintock even suggested a pheromone agent as a likely trigger, but others connected her research back to lunar synchronization. While the study initially appeared to have uncovered a unique social reproduction behavior, further tests confirmed no connection beyond random chance. Follow-up papers revealed flawed methodologies in the original study, which confirmed no synchronization at all.

Although examples of reproductive synchrony are found in the animal kingdom, including some primates, it has yet to be found in humans. This has not stopped anecdotal evidence from supporting such ideas even though more likely explanations exist. Stress and unusual sleep patterns in roommates with similar schedules are just as likely triggers for a perceived menstrual synchrony.

Anthropological arguments for menstrual synchrony being a remnant from the hunter-gatherer era also have been proved to be incorrect. Theoretically night-hunting activity might be timed to a full moon, and women who could synchronize their menstrual cycles to the Moon would likely produce more offspring. This ability would then be passed on to their daughters as a genetic adaptation, which would point to menstrual synchrony as a process of evolution, with the Moon being used as a means of synchronization. While the concept seems plausible, studies of isolated tribes that have similarities to early humans don't confirm it. Data collected from women of the Dogon tribe in West Africa shows no correlation of menstrual cycles. In hindsight, this makes sense, as a high number of births at specific times of the year would make such a tribe extremely vulnerable.

When held against scientific scrutiny, any connection of the Moon to fertility is disappointingly weak. Even turning to the science of anthropology doesn't help. Researchers conclude that there's no evidence to link the Moon to patterns of human reproduction. The similar durations are merely coincidental, and not all that similar. The belief simply grew out of a desire to make such a connection. It's no different from the basic concept of astrology. Human nature often waives rational arguments in favor of the more satisfying psychological alternative. This is a typically harmless route if it's not confused for reality. If the Moon can be a romantic symbol and empower women, there is justification for the sentiment. Symbiotic relationships between us and the Moon can enrich our lives. We need only remember the true nature of the bond.

When the Moon Ate the Sun

I n 585 B.C., two ancient kingdoms were at war in what is now known as Turkey. The ancient Lydians and the Medians had been at war for six years with no end in sight. On May 28, another indecisive battle began but was interrupted by an extraordinary event. As the evening approached, the skies darkened faster than expected as a solar eclipse passed through the area. Soldiers on both sides looked in wonder and fear as the Moon unexpectedly rose again from the west to cover the Sun and darken the skies. Believing it to be a supernatural warning, they laid down their weapons, and a truce was called. Soon after, two neighboring kings intervened to create a peace treaty, and the river valley where the warring soldiers had witnessed the solar eclipse became the new border. The eclipse had not only ended the battle, but it indirectly ended the war. It is the only known solar eclipse credited with creating peace.

The eclipse of 585 B.C. is also famous for being the first eclipse ever predicted, but the claim has always been controversial. This accomplishment was credited to Greek mathematician and astronomer Thales of Miletus, but exactly how he did it is unknown. Eclipses were poorly understood during Thales' time, and Thales lacked the precise geometry needed to make astronomical calculations. It's possible he might have been aware that eclipses repeat every 18.5 years from the Babylonians, but this alone wouldn't have been enough. That he predicted only the year of the eclipse and not the specific date indicates that it might have been a lucky guess.

Despite two very human stories, the Eclipse of Thales, as it's now known, still retains a mystical persona. Political fortunes and personal fate are the metaphysical hallmarks of solar eclipses and astrology in general, but the eclipse of 585 B.C. is significant for the real-world events it triggered. Fear gave way to peace, and Thales got lucky predicting an astronomical phenomenon that was well beyond his time. Ironically, even the attempt of predicting an eclipse resulted in a certain amount of good fortune. This happy accident aligns with the dual nature of the eclipses of antiquity. They were simultaneously viewed as historical and prophetic events.

Another early solar eclipse was documented in China in 1302 B.C. with an accurate and rather poetic description:

"Three flames ate the Sun and big stars were seen."

The "three flames" are thought to refer to the coronal flares seen near totality. These historic records show that solar eclipses and their impact were noticed all around the world. The earliest solar eclipse to be recorded by humans occurred in Ireland in the year 3340 B.C. with the record in a rock petroglyph, but the earliest solar eclipse described in writing was seen by the Babylonians in 1375 B.C. They also made the first scientific breakthrough with solar eclipses by establishing that they appear in cycles. The Saros cycle is still used in modern astronomy.

Eclipses may appear to be random and rare events, which adds to their mystique, but they occur regularly. Eclipses would happen every month if the Moon crossed exactly in front of the Sun, but due to a seven-degree tilt in its orbit, the shadow misses Earth most of the time. Only when the orbits of Earth and the Moon intersect can solar eclipses occur, and that only happens two or three times a year. Even then, not all are easily seen. Because Earth's surface is covered by 70 percent water, many solar eclipses go unnoticed because they occur over uninhabited parts of the world. As a result, many people live their entire lives without seeing one. Their rare appearances were interpreted as bad omens for kings and countries for thousands of years. Traditional lore attributed the death of King Henry I of England to a solar eclipse that crossed through England in 1131 A.D. Although he died the following year, a connection was made all the same

Even though they have been mathematically predicted from ancient times, solar eclipses remained a dramatic sign of mundane astrology, which dealt with the fortunes of countries. They were absolute proof that an event in the sky could affect events on the ground, so the fate of a country was thought to be determined or even undone by these bad omens. These astrological omens are found around the world and date back to at least the seventh century B.C., where ancient kings went into hiding for safety or performed atonement rituals when one was detected. A disturbance in the heavens was a sign that the gods were displeased and required a response. Even the word "disaster" is rooted in the Greek translation "bad star." But the prediction also could backfire, such as when Chinese astrologers were supposedly beheaded for missing an eclipse in 2137 B.C.

It's understandable that a general vagueness often was employed as a means of self-protection for court astrologers. Nothing specific was ever predicted because such things were essentially impossible to predict. An inherent sense of vagueness is found in astrology to this day, adding to its mystic appeal, and making it difficult to verify. The supposed bad result of an eclipse is just a psychological byproduct of positive pattern matching. When unexpectedly dramatic events occur, the brain chemically is stimulated to remember them in greater detail, simultaneously forming patterns with similarly timed events. Bad events can be guarded against, and good fortune can be encouraged. Coincidences are gathered into a false sense of order, and the unforeseen becomes manageable.

Without science, it was impossible to counter the mystical nature of eclipses, and astrology continued to flourish, but today historians use the predictive power of astronomy to learn about the past. The real power of historical eclipses is that they can be measured with extreme accuracy. Eclipses of the past can be calculated to a precision of seconds, and within just a few degrees of latitude and longitude. Historical events closely connected to eclipses now can be accurately dated. Therefore, solar eclipses don't predict the future as much as they reveal the past.

The Celestial Encyclopedia

A strology carries an air of forgotten knowledge akin to magic. Its arcane nature creates an aura of intrigue, but unlike other lost arts, its basic concepts have been meticulously compiled. Originally developed to advise ancient rulers, today's version of astrology originates from the Greeks, and specifically from the writings of a single author. What we know about the Moon, astrologically speaking, comes from the eminent Greek scholar Ptolemy.

Astrology arrived in Greece around 185 B.C. and was quickly adopted into its culture and philosophy. The Greeks were among the first to contemplate an overall philosophy of the world, and astrology was a natural fit. At the center of this view was Ptolemy, who lived in the city of Alexandria in the second century A.D. He worked in many areas of science but is most noted for his comprehensive writings. His two most famous works, which endured all the way into the late Middle Ages, were the *Almagest* and *Tetrabiblos*. Together they linked astronomy and astrology into a single science, setting the tone of believability.

The Almagest was the authoritative text on astronomy. It contained a complete collection of known astronomical knowledge, including a star catalog based on the work of the Greek astronomer Hipparchus. Although not as accurate as later star catalogs, its 48 constellations form the basis of the ones we use today, and the theories laid down in the *Almagest* would remain unchallenged until the time of Copernicus.

What the *Almagest* did for astronomy, the *Tetrabiblios* did for astrology. Loosely translated as four books, it was another comprehensive treatment explaining astrological signs as well as the planets and their predictive meaning. Many concepts, including the importance of the alignment of planets at birth, remain fundamental to modern astrology. Beyond a complete reference, the *Tetrabiblios* would also legitimize astrology as a benefit to medicine by connecting the two fields. It would be a required textbook in medical universities that doctors studied for centuries. This resulted in a certain tolerance from the Catholic Church, which otherwise did not approve of the implications that an individual life was predestined.

Based on Ptolemy's work, the Moon is grouped with the Sun and other classic planets to become one of seven celestial orbs, each one having influence over a different area of human life. The Moon was already credited with an influence on human fertility, so it was natural to give the planets related powers as well. This was a more systematic explanation of nature than mythology. The planets had powers like the gods they had once represented. The reaction of those influences could be deduced by use of logic and simple mathematics. This was the level of limited understanding available to Ptolemy at the time, but his conclusions were intuitive and contemplative. They made as much sense as they could.

The Moon in astrology has not changed that much from the days of Ptolemy. Typically, it's associated with emotions and the home, both traditional qualities of femininity. Due to its quick motion through the night sky, it's also credited with fast-changing events and the dreamy world of the subconscious. Many of these qualities have transcended the world of astrology to become the basic ideals we associate with it. The Moon often is seen as feminine and mysterious. While this is perfectly reasonable and even thoughtful, such associations shouldn't be confused with science. Astrology is an early attempt to establish a system of rules about nature, but it lacks any method of validation. It can make extraordinary predictive claims about the world that don't need to be verified, which is part of its enduring attraction. It attempts to answer questions that science can't.

From the 18th century onward, astrology diminished in importance but remained on the fringe of human enlightenment. Replaced by verifiable sciences, astrology shifted into an unusual curiosity that touched on the supernatural. It occasionally would regain popularity when generations became dissatisfied with technology, only to be labeled as an occult science by various church authorities. In the 20th century, astrology was transformed into a simpler and less threatening belief through daily horoscopes printed in virtually every newspaper. Anyone could get an astrological prediction if they knew their birth sign.

Ptolemy's influence on astronomy is hardly noticeable today. Grand systematic concepts have been replaced by simpler ideas. With lax definitions, there's no universal acceptance of what astrology is. Some casual believers enjoy identifying with the qualities associated with their sign and are perhaps even inspired by them. An Aquarius is a progressive humanitarian, or a Scorpio is resourceful and passionate. Others see it as a potential glimpse of self-help to make sense of their lives. Astrology lies in a state of blissful denial. Compared to other sciences, it offers no validation that it works, but most of us don't need it to.

The Age of Aquarius

Less than a month after half a billion people watched Neil Armstrong walk on the Moon, half a million gathered to experience another landmark symbol of the sixties. Woodstock was the antithesis of the Moon landing, and for those in attendance it held greater significance. The Moon landings were statements of hard science, national pride, and political power. Woodstock fans were seeking new forms of expression that broke with the establishment. The three-day rock concert held in mid-August was the signature event of 1969 and the closing chapter of the Summer of Love. It dismissed the hard science of rockets and national goals in favor of expressions of global love and peace. It was the rallying cry for a new age that combined global altruism with open-mindedness.

On Broadway, the counterculture movement gained a popular public persona with the musical *Hair*, which featured songs such as *Aquarius* and *Let the Sunshine In*. Those two songs were combined into a single hit called the *Age of Aquarius* by the pop band 5th Dimension. Released in spring of 1969, the song remained number one on the Billboard charts for six weeks, and it would become the second best-selling record of the year. It opens with an optimistic appraisal for the new age driven by a mystical refrain. The dawn of a new age was signaled in part by the Moon entering the seventh house. New partnerships were in the air, and the Moon was cool in a mysterious way.

Astrology continued in popularity beyond Woodstock and *Hair* much to the chagrin of scientists and astronomers. To them, astrology was nothing more than an elaborate ancient superstition, but that was part of its appeal. For stressful lives filled with uncertainty, it offered nonspecific but upbeat advice that didn't require validation. Beginning with a wave of New Age books in the seventies that embraced a holistic view, astrology gained some sense of credibility with connections to psychology and sociology. While daily horoscopes remained in play, the intellectual focus shifted to interpretations of personality traits and social interactions. This was especially relevant in an age where people were searching for a new self-identity and harmony in relationships. On this specific matter, science didn't have a good response. Love became a dominant issue with astrology, and the issues such as the interplay of Venus and the Moon in a horoscope became a prime concern.

Since the Moon plays a dominant role in astrology, it's easy to make a connection between a resurgence of astrology with the exploration of the Moon. Such poetic observations seem a natural part of astrology and are often used to support the basic premise, but this idea slips as we explore deeper into space. In classic astrology, the Sun, the Moon, and five other planets govern the 12 zodiac signs. As the solar system expanded, new planets were assigned to rule a sign of their own, with Uranus influencing Aquarius and Neptune controlling Pisces. When Pluto was discovered, it was similarly assigned to Scorpio, but Pluto's short duration as a planet makes its influence on the sign feel awkward and incomplete. It might be said that Pluto, which is known for its negative influence, has passed that troubling effect on to the study of astrology. While Pluto's demotion might seem to be a damaging blow, its effect does not seem permanent. Despite its misalignments, astrology goes on.

Shortly after their successful return, Apollo 13 astronauts Jim Lovell and Jack Swigert accepted an invitation to watch a performance of *Hair*. The astronauts were a natural guest choice for a show that professed a cosmic awareness. The crew had named their lunar module Aquarius to honor the dawning of a new age. They had listened to the show's music on the way to the Moon, but the live performance back on Earth was not as well received, and they left after the first act. When asked, Jack Swigert indicated he didn't appreciate the way the American flag was treated. As former military pilots, the sentiment was understandable. The musical's then-controversial anti-war theme was not part of its more congenial pop song rendition. Over time, the simple idea of love and understanding is the most common theme associated with the show and the era.

Even though it's specifically mentioned in *Hair*, the Age of Aquarius didn't technically start in the sixties. The lyrics "Moon in the Seventh House" and "Jupiter aligning with Mars" are not specific enough to trigger a new age. They are common events, and there is no astrological consensus on when the Age of Aquarius will actually start. It could be hundreds or even thousands of years away, but perhaps a precise answer does not matter. The Age of Aquarius is really the Age of Apollo, and it began as predicted. Much of the altruistic barrier breaking spirit has been captured in the global view that followed the Apollo Moon missions. We can seek guidance in the example of Aquarius as we strive for peace and harmony in the stars.

Moon Secret 8: D-Day was triggered by a Full Moon.

In the morning of June 6, 1944, the largest amphibious force ever assembled landed on the beaches of Normandy. Considered by many as the turning point of World War II, the invasion was specifically timed to coincide with a full moon, which gave the allied forces both a low tide and better illumination for locating landing zones. That night, 156,000 men went into battle, making it the most influential full moon in history.

Impressions

The sea is flecked with bars of grey
The dull dead wind is out of tune,
And like a withered leaf the moon
Is blown across the stormy bay.

OSCAR WILDE

JULY:
Real Lunacy

The Wolf Moon (Southern Hemisphere)

(How fear and ignorance can create an illusion)

Moonstruck

Pink Floyd's journey to the dark side began with a real trip to the Moon. Years before the release of its *Dark Side of the Moon* album, the band performed live for the BBC during the Apollo 11 Moon landing. On the night of the landing, British viewers were transported to the Moon with Moonhead, a live jam session filled with their trademark psychedelic sound. This moment has become an almost forgotten footnote in music history, and their acoustic ride to the Moon is overlooked in favor of the band's more famously titled work.

The *Dark Side of the Moon* has enjoyed legendary success. The iconic light prism album cover adorns posters and t-shirts over 40 years later. Released on the heels of the Apollo missions, a direct association is easy, but the title is an allusion to lunacy. The band was making a quiet tribute to its founding member Syd Barrett, who had succumbed to mental illness some years earlier. Although subtle, the title reaffirmed an ancient belief in lunacy. Even as Armstrong's footprint demystified the Moon, the prior connection to madness endured. In a variation of art imitating human nature, Pink Floyd's historic contribution is dwarfed by its more poetic endeavor.

With the aid of fiction and superstition, the Moon's link to madness has continued as a popular belief. As late as the 1800s, scientific studies still were attempting to establish a connection between mental illness and the Moon, and convicted criminals could plead for leniency if they could convince the courts that their crimes were committed near a full moon. Only a century previously, it was believed by some that a person could go insane or even die by sleeping outside under the light of a full moon. As the science of mental illness became better understood in the

20th century, the Moon no longer was considered an official cause, but stories of peculiar incidents persist in modern culture through anecdotal evidence.

Today, the myth of lunacy extends to nurses and police officers who reportedly believe that more medical emergencies and criminal activity occur around a full moon. These accounts have been circulated so often that they have become integral to the myth itself. The modern power of the Moon is validated by the experience of professionals who are in a better position to notice its unique influence. The conclusion would seem perfectly reasonable, but in reality, it carries no more weight than anyone else's personal opinions. Surveys of crime activity and its relationship to the Moon have been periodically conducted since the 1980s, and none have found any substantial evidence of a connection. Police officers and nurses are just as capable of drawing the same nonscientific conclusions as the rest of the general population.

These stories still catch our attention because they are entertaining. Though still mildly alluring, the idea of lunacy has lost its credibility for most of us. Whether or not we personally believe in lunacy, it remains such a strong part of our culture that it pops up all the time. The true power of the Moon stems from its original association with lunacy, which is shared throughout our collective conscience. Lunacy has transformed into a relatable meme of the 21st century and continues to be reinforced by other entertaining horror stories. The urban legends of lunacy are a familiar part of the Moon's persona, and there's no compunction to dismiss them outright. They are indulged as amusing diversions available to be reconnected with other myths. The Moon's reputation continues.

One might think that the stories of lunacy would have ended with Neil Armstrong walking on the Moon. Although traveling to the Moon was a stressful experience, all Apollo astronauts emerged from their journeys unscathed from a maximum lunar exposure. For some, the troubles began after their return. Buzz Aldrin struggled with depression after he left NASA, resulting in two failed marriages and a ruined career. Depression resulting in drug and alcohol abuse was also common among many of the astronauts' wives. It has been attributed to the unreasonable expectations placed upon them and a disconnect from their newly created celebrity husbands. It is a poignant illustration of mental health issues connected to real problems in our daily lives on Earth with any connection to the Moon's being coincidental.

Any of us can be susceptible to the power of the Moon, but the power of lunacy comes from us. The Moon holds a dramatic, glamorous, and magical reputation that is difficult to counter rationally. It is no accident that the Moon is associated with horror and fantasy stories. It represents the dark association of fear and nightmares by choice. The Moon is part of the explainable natural world, but we willingly elevate it to the supernatural simply because we enjoy it. From that appointed place, the Moon possesses an even greater power. Superstition and confirmation bias persist, and the irrational can make perfect sense if we choose.

A Moon by Any Other Name...

There is nothing either good or bad but thinking makes it so.

Hamlet act 2, scene 2

From ancient times, we have credited the Moon with two formidable powers: the ability to affect equally both ocean tides and our minds. It is a microcosm of a larger worldview where different layers of believability are intertwined. Tidal forces have a scientific explanation that unfortunately is rarely understood. Lunacy, on the other hand, lacks any scientific credulity, but often finds acceptance in our society.

The Moon remains a focal point of both science and lore. If Isaac Newton is responsible for the scientific view, then we might blame William Shakespeare for codifying its irrational side. Born less than 100 years apart, they are the authors of two competing foundations of thought. While our limited comprehension of the tides may be one reason we still believe in lunacy, the associated drama and intrigue might be another. We enjoy myths for their own sake. Even when they lack truth, they still have value.

"*The Ship of Fools*" is another lunacy myth that endures today mostly as poetic metaphor. Just like the Moon's most famous power, it grew from the popularization of a false conclusion. It refers to a nonexistent medieval tradition where townsfolk struck with mental illness routinely were rounded up and forced into maritime service. The likely origin of this fable is a misinterpretation of the famous painting Ship of Fools by Hieronymus Bosch, which had been inspired by a satirical play by Sebastian Brant. This mistaken assumption about lunacy oddly illustrates a basic lesson in human nature. Mysticism begins with a misunderstanding, and further association with other unknowns compounds the effect.

The Moon lies at the center of many irrational beliefs. It conveniently hangs in the night sky waiting to be credited with various inexplicable aspects of human nature. Over time, a veiled, enigmatic power becomes permanently cemented in our cultural psyche by memorable depictions in art and literature. The Moon's mystification has been a continuous feedback loop where core beliefs about the Moon inspire new generations of artists with similar ideas. The Moon regularly returns in stories as a reminder of a process.

As we read Shakespeare's plays today, we not only see how the Moon was viewed in Elizabethan times, but examples of how it became entrenched into our modern-day society. The Moon was frequently used by Shakespeare as a literary device and theatrical prop with references to both love and dread. Elizabethans might have held more superstitious beliefs than us, but they obviously understood the idea of expressions for dramatic purposes. Those classic themes about the Moon repeatedly have been employed by successive authors because they continue to find a receptive audience. The Moon is our guilty pleasure. We are the writers of the Moon's theatrical presence in our lives and enjoy endowing it with supernatural powers.

In *Romeo and Juliet*, we find the Moon alongside the famed couple when they first declare their love. From her balcony, Juliet warns Romeo not to swear his oath of love by the Moon because of its ever changing and inconsistent nature.

O, swear not by the moon, th' inconstant moon,
That monthly changes in her circle orb,
Lest that thy love prove likewise variable.

Romeo and Juliet, Act 2, Scene 2

The Moon's appearance marks the beginning of their doomed romance. In other plays, the Moon likewise could be blamed for any other irrational behavior. Othello ponders that the maddening doom of the Moon is not only fated for people but for the Moon itself. The Moon tragically is faulted for being too close to Earth:

> It is the very error of the moon,
> She comes more nearer earth than she was wont
> And makes men mad.
>
> *Othello,* Act 5, Scene 2

Like many standard tropes, the Moon's infamous powers are well rooted in Shakespeare, but this may not be a case of art imitating nature. While Shakespeare's Moon plays its part sufficiently as an instigator of human passion, it almost is always limited to being a symbolic metaphor. Shakespeare's characters mostly mark the Moon as an object of fantasy for the sheer sake of entertainment. If this treatment can be taken as a reliable account of how Elizabethans saw the Moon, then their feelings about the Moon weren't so different from our own contemporary views. The Moon's implied influence was mostly symbolic.

The downfall of Shakespeare's lead characters is always based on a tangible personality flaw or past event. This is clearly the case in Hamlet, his most famous play to address mental instability. The mystery of Hamlet's possible "affliction" frequently is contemplated within the play, but the Moon is never blamed for it. In fact, the Moon is never mentioned once. Literature is only the chronicle of the fantastic ideas surrounding lunacy, but not the source of the belief. It is just part of the complex web that embeds such beliefs in our collective consciousness and leaves them attractively plausible.

The Gothic Moonrise

n Shelley's *Frankenstein*, the Moon witnesses the birth of a monster:

"The moon gazed on my midnight labours..."

It also reveals the dread reality of Victor's creation:

"When, by the dim and yellow light of the moon, as it
forced its way through the window shutters, I beheld the
wretch—the miserable monster whom I had created."

The Moon initially seems friendly to the monster as it guides him
and keeps him company as he walks through the woods. His response
is genuinely human:

"Soon a gentle light stole over the heavens and gave me
a sensation of pleasure. I started up and beheld a radiant
form rise from among the trees. I gazed with a kind of
wonder."

As the story takes a darker turn, the Moon returns to its stereotypical
characterization. It repeatedly appears right before an act of violence,
adding a sense of suspense while reinforcing an association with terror,
evil, and madness. Through regular exposure to the Moon, the reader
experiences the monster's loss of humanity and Victor's vengeful path

to insanity. The Moon's power to cause lunacy eventually is fulfilled. Within *Frankenstein*, our most sensationalized views of the Moon come to life, and Shelley creates a textbook for using the Moon as an icon of horror. The visual cues are so well known today that they've become clichés.

Classic monsters were born in the Victorian era out of necessity. Literacy among the middle class had increased during the Industrial Revolution, and ghost stories were a popular choice to handle the new demand. Adopted from a shared folklore, they were easy to adapt and print in bulk. In cinema, they were popularized again during classic horror eras of the 1920s and 1950s, where they retained all their original gothic trappings. Haunted houses were now synonymous with Victorian architecture, and a full moon was an expected backdrop. Just like novels that had preceded them, there was a steady demand for films that were relatively inexpensive to produce. With a steady output of classic horror films, old beliefs about the Moon were retold and magnified.

The Moon is similarly used in Bram Stoker's *Dracula*. In the opening chapter, it is set dressing during a wolf attack, alluding to its more famous power to transform into a werewolf:

> "All at once the wolves began to howl as though the
> moonlight had some peculiar effect on them."

The Moon then continues to make a regular appearance throughout the book with heavy emphasis on the dramatic and ghostly effect of moonlight:

> "The moonbeams seemed to quiver as they went by me
> into the mass of gloom beyond. More and more they
> gathered till they seemed to take dim phantom shapes . . .
> I fled, and felt somewhat safer in my own room, where
> there was no moonlight"

When finally revealed, the vampires have no immediate association to the Moon beyond the observation that they cast no shadow in moonlight. Even then, the Moon suggests their otherworldly presence by highlighting this eerie detail. This visual staging of the Moon continued in cinema with *Nosferatu*, one of the earliest horror movies filmed in 1922. Gothic horror novels depend heavily on crisp visual language to build suspense, and those visual cues easily are transferred to film. As vampire stories evolved, the ever-present Moon expanded into their mythology. Moonlight eventually offered a restorative power for a weakened or destroyed vampire, and a chance to extend the story. Some observant fans have argued that this makes little sense since moonlight is just bounced sunlight and should have the same destructive effect, but such logic doesn't apply within a horror film. More than a theatrical light source, the Moon's spooky nature had been utilized as an additional story element.

Culturally, the Moon's power of lunacy overwhelmingly is associated with the werewolf, but that dominant connection is mostly due to film. Werewolves were a common folktale that had no single defining novel. The gothic era is filled with adaptations including *A Story of a Weir-Wolf* by Catherine Crowe in 1846, one of the earliest horror stories penned by a woman; *Wagner. the Wehr-Wolf* by George W. M. Reynolds in 1846; and *The Wolf Leader* by Alexandre Dumas in 1857. Each story tells a completely different version of the werewolf myth, but none of them use the Moon as a trigger for a monster transformation. The legend of the full moon was born in the first werewolf films, *Werewolf of London* in 1935 and *The Wolf Man* in 1941. The latter introduces a famous poem that was repeatedly used in subsequent films:

> Even a man who is pure in heart
> and says his prayers by night
> may become a wolf when the wolfbane blooms
> and the autumn moon is bright.

As the gothic age closed, Robert Louis Stevenson created an updated version of the werewolf story. Published in 1886, *Strange Case of Dr. Jekyll and Mr. Hyde* is horror with a science-fiction twist. Dr. Jekyll is a man of science, and the transformation between man and monster results from his own experiment. Ancient dark magic is replaced with a modern serum, and the Moon's influence is limited to storytelling. There is no need to draw power from the Moon. The monster is a creation of technology, a theme shared with *Frankenstein* and many other horror stories since.

Gothic tales have secured a permanent home in our cultural language despite an incongruence with science. That is part of their charm and success. Whether the genre is horror, science fiction, or comic books, we look for heroes and villains to tell the stories that science can't, but once in a while there can be an overlap between the two worlds. After creating *Frankenstein*, Mary Shelley noted she had been inspired by the frightful sight of the Moon appearing through a window one night. This origin story has become a legend to the point of being doubted, but this is a rare instance of a horror myth that can be scientifically collaborated.

The location and likely dates of Shelley's encounter with the Moon are well known. She was staying with friends in June 1816 at the Villa Diodati, which overlooks Lake Geneva, Switzerland. In 2014, a group of astronomers from Texas State University led by Donald Olsen confirmed that a bright gibbous Moon would have shone directly into Mary Shelley's bedroom window around 2 a.m. on the morning of June 16. The story that inspired a horror legend is true. Just like many of us, Mary Shelley was startled by the Moon, an unexpected bright light in the middle of the night. Thus, the Moon ushered in the birth of modern horror stories, and our artistic interpretations would continue to feed our sensationalized view of lunacy.

A Bump in the Night

Beyond lunacy, scientists have searched for a natural explanation behind our fear of the Moon. There may not be a single definitive cause. The answer may simply be one of association. We fear the unknown in the dark, and the Moon is most notable at night. It rises and sets like the Sun and stars, though never quite in a predictable way. Its unusual behavior demands an explanation from our rational mind, but simple intuition does not provide one. Strong enough to cast a slight shadow, but barely enough to see movement in the dark, it both encourages and denies us. Cut off from the reality of daytime, our imagination runs free and is dominated by our strongest emotions.

For early humans, a full moon might have acted as a threat assessment. One study shows that lions are more likely to attack prey shortly after the setting of a full moon. The sudden shift in illumination gives nocturnal predators an advantage. The Moon might have been a warning to coastal dwellers against dangerous high tides. In such cases, a full moon would have produced elevated levels of unease that could have built up eventually to become a more generalized fear. Taken separately, these theories don't explain the universal fear associated with the Moon, but they show how easy it is to associate different dangers with the Moon. The Moon reminds us of our vulnerability.

Even without concrete evidence, we likely can still trace our irrational fear of the dark, and by extension the Moon, to the dawn of civilization. With the combination of language to tell stories and outdoor fires, the stage was set to create drama, which included tales built out of fears. Heightened emotions, darkness, and the Moon would have become easily connected through stories. As our civilization grew, the Moon's fictional influence would continue to expand to where it was credited with powers it didn't have.

The Moon's supernatural powers can be traced as far back as ancient Rome, where it already was associated with many gods. Hecate was especially noteworthy as a three-formed goddess, with each form representing a phase of the Moon. She was associated with magic, sorcery, and ghosts; many well-known dark powers of the Moon are descended from her. As mythology made way for Christianity in the Middle Ages, the Moon lost its deification, but the original supposed purpose of the Moon remained. Hecate is directly referenced in Shakespeare's *A Midsummer Night's Dream* and *Macbeth*, where the titular character notes,

> Witchcraft celebrates pale Hecate's offerings.
> *Macbeth*, act 2, scene 1

Hecate appears later in the play among witches to predict Macbeth's eventual doom.

Witches and werewolves once were considered one and the same, in that both possessed the power to change into an animal form at will. Tapping the power of the full moon was a means of transformation. The prevailing belief was that werewolves would feed on the innocent as they strayed into dark forests at night. Witch and werewolf trials once ran rampant through many parts of Europe. Sometimes, such attacks would have been considered nothing more than horrible cases of mass murders in today's world. Others turned out to be a one-sided tale of folktale-driven hysteria akin to the Salem witch trials. Either way, the Moon was eyed with suspicion as it was considered the source of an evil power, and therefore an acceptable scapegoat for terrible events.

We are not creatures of the night. Nocturnal animals, such as cats, owls, and wolves, often are credited with having special imaginary powers like the Moon, since they share a realm that we don't understand. With civilization, we have extended our ability to function at night, but we're diurnal by nature. When isolated, we sleep with a naturally heightened sense of danger. Combined with the biological mechanism that triggers us to awaken with the morning light, many of us find it difficult to sleep under a bright light. This has been documented in extreme northern communities that experience very long days and nights. Similarly, the light of a full moon can induce restlessness. A lack of sleep often leads to emotional distress, which sometimes may trigger extreme symptoms for those who suffer from depression and bipolar disorders. This leads to our greatest fear of the Moon: losing control of one's mind.

The Confounding Seas

An old fable says that Aristotle drowned himself at the Straits of Euripus while trying to solve the mystery of the tides. In an act of frustration, he cast himself into the seas while uttering these last poetic words:

"Comprehend me, since I cannot comprehend thee!"

Aristotle's words and dying act suggest a lost cause between the forces of reason and chaos, perhaps resulting in his own suicidal madness. The ultimate hero of rational thought is pitted against an unfathomable force that costs him his life. More than just his life, the death could be viewed as an act of insanity. It reads as a fateful, tragic tale of losing everything while trying to understand the incomprehensible.

This fictional death was likely the invention of later Greeks who imagined more fitting endings for their legendary heroes. Many other famous ancient philosophers had equally colorful deaths. There may be a bit of truth to the fable, as Aristotle spent his final years near Euripus, but he never truly solved the mystery of the tides. He suspected the tides were driven by an unexplained tilting of the surrounding landscape. It's important to note that the tides at the Straits of Euripus were famously unpredictable, but Aristotle's inability to find a solution adds to the inexplicable aura of the seas and the Moon that controls them. From Aristotle to Galileo to Newton, an explanation has been sought and often missed by some of the most famous thinkers in history. Even today, the Moon's best-known ability remains its least understood.

Ocean water bulges up on the sides of our planet that face either directly to or away from the Moon. We experience high tides twice a day as Earth's rotation spins us through these bulges, but attributing them to the Moon's gravity alone is an oversimplification that can lead to doubt and nonscientific conjectures. The common textbook explanation of the tides is technically incorrect. Tides are not the result of the magnetic-like attraction of the Moon. If they were, we would see the same effect in smaller bodies of water. Objects also would be physically lighter when the Moon is directly overhead.

The key to understanding the tides is found at the points along Earth's that face at right angles to the Moon's position. At these locations, the Moon is below the horizon. Its pull on the ocean water is slightly downward relative to the Moon's pull on the planet. The oceans respond like huge bags of water by squeezing in the opposite direction. Their shape is more a result of a push than a direct pull.

Tides do not appear precisely 12 hours apart. The Moon's motion in orbit causes a slight lag to the cycle as it constantly advances its position in the sky, adding 50 more minutes to a complete tidal sequence, or 12 hours and 25 minutes between each high tide. The Sun's gravity also causes a similar tidal effect, but is only about 46 percent as strong as the influence of the Moon. When the Sun and Moon align during a new or full moon, the result is an especially high tide known as a spring tide. Not to be confused with the season of spring, they occur twice a month. They are a rare example of a full moon truly affecting nature, but a nearly identical effect is seen during a new moon.

The phenomenon of tides is complex with the Moon's gravity only being the initial trigger. The shape of Earth's landmasses and coastlines contributes heavily toward their varying frequency and height. Perhaps Aristotle's idea about landscapes was right in a small way, even though his reasoning was off. Similarly, Galileo's explanation of tides also was mostly flawed with just a glimmer of truth. He thought tides were driven by the Sun with the addition of an unusual sloshing or oscillation effect. This is sometimes called one of Galileo's greatest mistakes, but ironically it was an attempt to find a rational explanation that defied the mysticism already associated with the Moon. As noted above, the Sun's influence is less than half of the Moon's, but there is an actual lagging effect in the tides. Earth's rotation is too fast for all the ocean water to keep up. The result is a set of tidal nodes, or intersections, at different global locations where the ocean swells back and forth.

Isaac Newton finally showed how tides resulted from gravity, but even his explanation didn't take irregular coastlines and tidal nodes into account. It was French mathematician Pierre-Simon Laplace who expanded on Newton's work to calculate the tidal forces at different locations around the world. Continuing the work of Laplace, Lord Kelvin categorized tidal patterns into ten distinct recurring components and created an analog computer to calculate them in 1872. Our modern understanding of tides is far more complex than Aristotle could have realized, but there is a rational explanation. Even though it's complex, it should not be confused as a mystic power of the Moon.

Ironically, it was Aristotle who first gave a false lead on with lunacy while other ancient Greek scholars were noticing its tidal effects. The Greek geographer Pytheas of Massalia first attributed a tidal effect to the Moon while surveying the Atlantic coastlines around the third century B.C. This same conclusion was reached by the Greek astronomer Seleucus of Seleucia in 150 B.C.

Three hundred years later, the Roman historian Pliny the Elder linked the two lunar influences. Lunacy resulted from the liquid nature of the human brain, which made it susceptible to the powers of the Moon. The brain was a fishbowl-sized ocean, complete with its own tides. Ludicrous as this sounds, the argument is still offered as a logical reason for lunacy. While explanations of tidal effects remained speculative for centuries, the belief in the Moon's psychological influence grew. Stacking additional beliefs on top of a false conclusion is a consistent human folly. Creating myths about lunacy is a product of a fertile imagination and a willingness to believe beyond reason. Perhaps that is a more fitting definition of lunacy.

Moon Secret 9: 100 Miniature Bibles have landed on the Moon.
Astronaut Ed White had stated a desire to take a Bible to the Moon,
but that hope was sadly cut short by his death during an Apollo 1 accident. In response to that tragedy, Reverend John Stout, who worked at
NASA, fulfilled White's wish on a later mission. The King James Bible
already was commercially available in microfilm form no bigger than a
postage stamp. Starting with Apollo 12, several attempts were made to
land miniaturized Bibles on the Moon. Due to early mistakes and the
Apollo 13 accident, the first efforts failed to deliver a Bible to the Moon's
surface, but with Apollo 14, a hundred Bibles successfully landed on
the Moon and were returned to Earth. They later became known as the
First Lunar Bibles.

Lunar Paraphrase

The moon is the mother of pathos and pity.
When, at the wearier end of November,
Her old light moves along the branches,
Feebly, slowly, depending upon them;—
WALLACE STEVENS

AUGUST:
The Leap of Faith

The Old Moon (South African)

(How going to the Moon changed religion and how it didn't)

A Spiritual Bond

Soon after watching live coverage of the first Moon walk, Pope Paul VI offered his papal blessing over the radio as part of the first religious message directed into space:

> "Here, from his Observatory at Castel Gandolfo, near Rome, Pope Paul VI is speaking to you astronauts: Honor, greetings and blessings to you, conquerors of the moon. Pale lamp of our nights and our dreams bring to her with your living presence the voice of the Spirit."

Speaking to the astronauts was a symbolic gesture as they could not hear the message live, but Pope Paul VI's sincerity was genuine. Just like Neil Armstrong, he was taking a leap into a new world, and it was one he was willing to take. Months earlier, he had mentioned the upcoming Apollo mission in his official addresses. On the previous night, he had gazed at the Moon using the telescope at the Vatican Observatory. He later would watch the Moon Landing broadcasts on a television beneath the same telescope. Armstrong's first step was greeted with a spontaneous clap of joy from the pope who offered words of encouragement and support:

> "We are close to you with our good wishes and with our prayers, together the whole Catholic Church."

He would proclaim the event as "a sublime victory" for humanity in a later address but asked his listeners for a continued effort in solving the problems of the world.

A few months later, the entire crew of Apollo 11, along with their wives, embarked on what was dubbed the "Great Leap Tour." The highly successful trip covered 27 cities in 38 days and was greeted by massive crowds wherever it went. Diverse religious doctrines seemed inconsequential. Turnouts in traditionally devout countries such as Mexico and India were overwhelming. The crowd in Bombay, India, was estimated at 1.5 million strong. Approximately halfway through the tour, the crew stopped off at the Vatican. The Pope complimented Neil Armstrong on his choice of words to mark the first step and in exchange was gifted his own moon rock.

An unexpected bond occurred between NASA and the Catholic Church, the two preeminent global symbols of science and religion. There was a shared perspective that offered hope for world peace and cooperation for the betterment of all people. Such a goal had long been a part of Pope Paul VI's agenda, but NASA had transitioned into it during the Apollo program. The urgency to become a world leader in rocket technology had been realized, but the astronauts had discovered Earth and its people from a new point of view. They went from national heroes to world ambassadors and, in doing so, represented all religions.

Back in the United States, the Moon missions also found solid support from religious faiths that included firmly conservative groups. Early on, there had been a concern that mankind didn't have the right to encroach on what had traditionally been considered God's domain. This sentiment was captured in the opinion of future Mormon Church leader Joseph Fielding Smith, Jr.:

> "It is doubtful that man will ever be permitted to make
> any instrument or ship to travel through space and visit
> the moon or any distant planet."

In short, astronauts would never make it to the Moon because God had not destined them to do so. In the glowing aftermath of Apollo's success, such negative criticism was trivialized and quickly forgotten. Fielding had a change of heart and admitted, somewhat quietly, that he had been wrong. He later would be presented with a Utah state flag that had flown to the Moon on Apollo 15. A victory for the United States was reinterpreted as a stand against the Soviet Union, which was vilified for its "godless communism." National patriotism and religious ideals were aligned, and NASA found a precarious sweet spot between science and religion.

Fielding's original prediction might seem antiquated today, but his response was based on concerns about how future space travel might have affected religious convictions. Colonies on other worlds and even the possibility of alien civilizations were unknowns to what had always been an Earth-centric faith. Once lunar missions were a reality, the apparent threat to religion was discounted. Religion functioned the same in space as it did back on Earth.

Since that time, many astronauts have shared their spiritual experiences in space, but the science of Apollo is occasionally still seen as an ideological enemy. Returned moon rocks have since confirmed a geologic history that is challenging to biblical literacy. A well-worn response since the days of Galileo has been to admonish science as a godless enemy, but the question is a matter of faith. Galileo, Newton, and many scientists have all taken a leap of faith in discovering the universe. By going to the Moon, our world which includes religion is illuminated by science, and our faith continues.

The Stretch of Reality

Toward the end of the second day of Apollo 11's mission, the crew passed a critical milestone. Like all other journeys to the Moon, the spacecraft shifted from the gravitational pull of Earth to that of the Moon. The moment was unseen by the public, and unfelt by the crew, which slept through it, but it was a pivotal part of the mission. Apollo 11 deliberately had traveled slightly slower than Earth's escape velocity. The Moon's gravity was required to leave Earth behind and complete the journey.

Although such an experience is limited to Apollo astronauts, the shift mirrors a change in our shared reality. Our perspective has expanded from a limited earthbound experience to one where we can see the universe. As we've grown in sophistication, science has been slowly adopted into our daily lives. A major part of this transformation can be connected back to the Moon as it began with Isaac Newton's law of gravity and ended with a journey to the Moon. We may not feel the effect of every scientific advancement, but the result is the same. Regardless of individual beliefs, we live in a world where science is as undeniable as gravity.

The discovery of gravity is often cited as the birth of modern physics, and yet if you had asked Isaac Newton how old the Moon was, his answer would have been based strictly on his Christian beliefs. The mixture of science and Bible literacy was a sign of Newton's times. Gravity explained how the Moon worked, but a related science didn't yet exist to describe the Moon's origin. Today, science or a lack of science, often defines a schism between the allegorical Old-Earth and the literal Young-Earth interpretations of creationism.

It's hard to believe that Newton's contribution to science was ever controversial, but it had its share of opponents and supporters. An unlikely pairing of each was George Berkeley and Thomas Bayes. In this case, Newton's work was supported by a religious thinker instead of being opposed. The challenge came from George Berkeley, an Irish philosopher who objected to Newton's work. Berkeley's theory of subjective realism, a concept where commonplace objects only existed in the mind, challenged Newton's work of deduced reality. Bayes, a presbyterian minister, published his only science-related work to specifically defend Newton against the attacks of Berkeley. For science, it is a minor note compared to the revolutionary theory that bears his name. He never published what became known as Bayes' theorem, but the fact that he used one of his two published works to defend Newton adds him to a group of people that successfully found a way to combine science and religion.

Bayes' theorem is the mathematics of determining the probability of an event based on prior knowledge of related events. Today, it plays a critical part in the development of AI but also provides us with an objective method to judge the likelihood of an idea being true and therefore real. It is likely that Bayes didn't realize the full potential of his work. It was only found after his death by a friend, Richard Price, who expanded on it. From there, it was French mathematician Pierre-Simon Laplace who saw its amazing potential. Laplace saw Bayes' theorem as a means to fill in gaps in knowledge. What was not known with certainty could be deduced with increasing percentages of probability until eventually it became all but certain. This process mimics the world of modern scientific research.

That Newton, who sometimes is credited as the founder of modern science, was defended by a man of faith may seem ironic, but there was common ground. Bayesian mathematics is not only the basis of the modern scientific process, but Bayes' theorem also encourages us to evaluate ideas based on evidence and not unrelated conjectures. It is a logical method to test the reality of a situation without bias. It shows us how best to measure the stretch of a new proposal and how to deal with its conclusions.

Bayes believed in a world determined by rules that only were partially understood, but the model of reality could be updated as more information became available. That which is not understood, does not invalidate the accepted model. The theorem is the basis of updating the certainty of belief based on evidence. It also minimizes the importance of prior belief, where an idea is assumed to be true or false without any corroborating evidence. This aspect of Bayes' theorem makes an important observation about the human condition. It counters our natural tendencies of blind faith by showing a tested result is more important than a prior untested assumption.

Bayes' theorem has found many diverse applications in modern science. Some of those have been applied directly to the Moon. Bayesian analysis is a specialized statistical procedure that can be used to extract meaningful information out of raw data. It has been used to improve the signal quality of laser light bounced off the Moon that offers a precise distance measurement to the Moon. It's also been used to determine if a full moon has any impact on Asian stock market prices. This is an example of a Bayesian inference that is used in artificial intelligence. Computers evaluate situations using mathematics and not intuition. This often can be in stark contrast to our intuitive reasoning skills where we are often unwilling to reconsider a belief based on new evidence.

Bayes was not the first scientist to find a coexistence between science and religion, but his actions represent a shift in how we see the world. From Copernicus to Newton, we cumulatively reached an understanding of the universe based on the work of scientists who often remained tied to theology. Bayes' theorem encapsulates their progress, but his defense of Newton demonstrates a critical ability to distinguish faith from science. The Moon helped define gravity, and Bayes defended that discovery. The universe of science is a part of our daily lives. By the time astronauts used the Moon's gravity to escape from Earth, our functional world was at odds with indoctrinated views. Assigning an age to the Moon based on scripture interpretations, just as Newton once did, stretches reality beyond reconciliation. Journeying to the Moon in such a world would be impossible.

According to Science...

I n 1940, Walt Disney released Fantasia, an ambitious collection of animated shorts set to classical music. Appearing regularly throughout the film, the Moon takes on many guises, from familiar links to Grecian gods in Beethoven's lyrical pastoral symphony to an icon of the supernatural in Mussorgsky's terror-filled *Night on Bald Mountain*. Easily missed as a minor visual transition, its appearance in Igor Stravinsky's *The Rite of Spring* is especially noteworthy for being one of the earliest depictions of a solar eclipse in film.

True to the nature of the segment, the Moon seen as an object of science as *The Rite of Spring* is a departure from the other segments. It poetically reinterprets its title to tell the story of the beginnings of life on Earth in purely scientific terms. Host Deems Taylor, who was a well-known music critic at the time, clearly states this factual approach at the beginning of the piece:

> "It's a coldly accurate reproduction of what science thinks..."

The choice of wording cleverly left room for interpretation on the potential controversial subject of evolution. If needed, whatever followed could be dismissed by the viewer as the belief of scientists. What followed was a parade of early life that climaxed with the world of the dinosaurs. Similar to the minor part it would play in the ideological war between science and biblical literacy, the Moon remained in the background. It's only briefly seen in two transitional scenes. Dinosaurs took the center stage and would become the major challenge to creationism.

While they had been popularized before, Disney's The Rite of Spring marked the entrance of dinosaurs into a new mass media. Their fossilized remains already were hard to deny, but now they had a relatable context. Generations of 20th-century children grew up on images of dinosaurs. Fantasia gave them an appealing look and a dramatic story. It was the beginning of the popularity of evolutionary science and a pivotal point in how our society addressed science.

The modern divide between scientific and religious interpretations of Earth's origin can be traced back to the time of Isaac Newton. Fundamentalism, the more rigid interpretation of creation, was a direct response to the Age of Enlightenment, and Newton's work marks the beginning of that time. This era, which some cite as running from the beginning of Newton's work in 1687 to the start of the French Revolution in 1789, is known for many things including the beginnings of geology. James Hutton presented a paper in 1785 called the "Theory of the Earth," in which he showed comprehensive evidence that Earth was thousands of times older than suspected.

The enlightened movement also inspired new philosophies. It encouraged the questioning of standard doctrines and had a growing effect of liberalism within the church. The response of some churches was to guard against it by sharply redefining their fundamental beliefs. By 1910, a collection of essays called The Fundamentals began circulating through American churches. This was the basis of Christian fundamentalism, out of which modern Evangelicalism would grow. On interpretations of the Bible, fundamentalism was very clear. The Bible was a literal truth, and the concept became so strong in society that the expression "the Gospel truth" became synonymous with an undeniable fact.

Such an approach certainly made sense when it came to addressing liberalism within the Church itself. All questions about the Church, God, and the world would be addressed in the simplest, most literal way possible. The result was a return to an intellectual time before Newton, where the Bible could be treated as a series of factual statements. Initially, this was easy to do as scientific discoveries in chemistry, physics, and geology were very abstract and didn't have a direct effect on everyday life. As scientific concepts grew in sophistication in the 20th century, speculations on the Moon's origin or Earth's could still be met with a degree of skepticism. Theories were just educated guesses that could be easily dismissed.

The Moon is rarely mentioned in the Bible. Even in Genesis, it's more of an afterthought. Just as in *The Rite of Spring*, it remains in the background. Going to the Moon changed all that. We embraced the event as easily as animated dinosaurs, and ensuing discoveries would lead to a new origin for the Moon and Earth. The aftermath of the Apollo program also proved consequential. It was rooted in 20th-century science that has since defined the origin of life. The narrative presented within *The Rite of Spring* has been confirmed. What scientists believe is a reality we all share whether we realize it or not. A cell phone is connected to the age of Earth. A genetic test is connected to the science of evolution.

Many religious sects, notably the Catholic Jesuits, have a high devotion to science. They see science as a means of religious enlightenment, to become closer to God through a better understanding of the universe. For them, it's also a matter of faith. Going to the Moon made it a contemporary object with simple and undeniable facts, but religious validation can still be found for those who are searching. Many astronauts who went to the Moon had a religious background, and some have stated that the experience has strengthened their religious convictions. Science took them to the Moon, and faith continued the journey.

Of Heaven and Earth

Two and a half hours after landing on the Moon and long before the first Moon walk, Buzz Aldrin of Apollo 11 made the following announcement:

"This is the LM pilot. I'd like to take this opportunity
to ask every person listening in, whoever and wherever
they may be, to pause for a moment and contemplate the
events of the past few hours and to give thanks in his or
her own way."

The process of landing on the Moon had made for a long day, and NASA had ordered rest. Aldrin, an elder at the Webster Presbyterian Church in Houston, planned to celebrate the moment with a communion ceremony. This was no trivial feat as it had taken considerable effort for it to be even possible. Aldrin needed to get permission from his minister and NASA to perform the ceremony, and he had to devise a way to bring what he needed onboard. His portable communion set included a small silver chalice that would fit among his personal effects. He started the ceremony with a scripture reading of his own choice.

I am the vine; you are the branches. Whoever remains
in me, and I in him, will bear much fruit; for you can do
nothing without me.
John 15:5

The first communion on the Moon has since gained some notoriety as a symbol of a religious stance amid science. It even has been suggested that NASA actively tried to hide or discourage it. While not widely publicized, it had been announced in the newspapers on the day of the launch. Deke Slayton, NASA's director of flight operations, had given Aldrin clearance but asked that he keep the wording of his announcement general. NASA was facing a lawsuit from an earlier reading of the Bible during a live broadcast from Apollo 8 and didn't want to complicate the situation. Aldrin reluctantly agreed. At the time, he wanted to capture the enormity of the moment with something spiritual, but in hindsight, he came to question the benefit of doing the service: "*We had come to space in the name of all mankind—be they Christians, Jews, Muslims, animists, agnostics, or atheists, but at the time I could think of no better way to acknowledge the Apollo 11 experience than by giving thanks to God.*"

The chalice used by Aldrin returned to Earth and is lovingly held by the Webster Presbyterian Church. It's still regularly used to commemorate the event on the Sunday closest to July 20, known locally as Lunar Communion Sunday. Although not official, it marks a new religious holiday, the day when religion extended into space to become part of the Moon. The faithful can take solace in the fact that hours before a man walked on the Moon, another man prayed on the Moon. He prayed in thanks for the opportunity to learn and explore—the very essence of the Apollo program.

Aldrin was not the first astronaut to pray in space nor was he the last. He was one of many who made a spiritual connection in space. During an interview on the return flight, he summarized the experience by paraphrasing another biblical scripture, Psalm 8:3-4. Appropriately, this was the same quote that Pope Paul VI had sent to the Moon as a handwritten message:

When I see your heavens, the work of your fingers,
the moon and stars that you set in place.
What is mankind that you are mindful of him,
human beings that you care for them?

Psalm 8:3-4

In a Post-Apollo world, there is an opportunity for a new leap of faith. Lunar communion was the start of a new spiritual awakening. For the faithful, it can remind us that our curiosity and a need to understand are part of a God-given nature. Not only were we destined for the Moon, but we are meant to go beyond. Ultimately, we are destined to explore the universe and understand its workings. The Moon has taught us that spirituality is not limited to Earth. From distant stars to subatomic particles and everything in between, our faith has no bounds.

PART 4:

AUTUMN
The Moon and Us

While science fiction has glamorized alien worlds, the Moon may be the key in defining the value of our world and add extra meaning to our lives.

September: Alien Moons
October: Beyond the Moon
November: Children of Moon

Moon Secret 10: The Moon is massive for a moon.
Earth's Moon is one of the largest moons in the solar system. It is second only to Ganymede in size and Io in density. If the Moon orbited Jupiter or Saturn, it would be easily visible through a telescope. If the Moon orbited Mars instead, it could be seen with the naked eye. The Moon has been photographed from the surface of Mars and appears as a gray dot alongside the brighter blue dot of Earth.

The Moon
The stars about the lovely moon
Fade back and vanish very soon,
When, round and full, her silver face
Swims into sight, and lights all space.
SAPPHO

SEPTEMBER:
Alien Moons

The Chrysanthemum Moon (Chinese)

(The moons of sci-fi reveal a truth stranger fiction)

Moons to Spare

Walking on the Moon was a rare moment in history when a science-fiction dream was utterly fulfilled by a technological achievement. For a brief time, it stood optimistically as precedent for a block of like-minded ideas. World-changing revolutions in computer and communication technology followed, but many common themes of science fiction remain fantasies. A world filled with autonomous robotic assistants and flying cars is a lot farther away than first predicted. Concepts such as faster-than-light (FTL) travel are speculative. Even routine trips to the Moon are not likely to happen soon.

The end of Apollo popped the sci-fi bubble. With basic lunar exploration achieved, trends in science fiction shifted. Stories about going to the Moon rapidly decreased in the 1970s. Life on worlds beyond our solar system became the predominant setting, either in our distant future or fabricated reality where details about exotic propulsion systems could be conveniently glossed over. Science fiction would still be influenced by real space exploration as alien landscapes where often enriched with images returned from exploring probes.

Geographic features of early fictional worlds often were scarce and planets with a single global environment were common. The planets Arrakis and Caladan from *Dune* are classic examples of desert and oceanic worlds. A planet encased in a single city was also a common theme. Fictional moons were initially rare unless used as a plot point. One of the moons of Arrakis has a strong magnetic field that makes a standard compass useless. As the Voyager space probes returned detailed images from the moons of Jupiter and Saturn, the concept of habitable moons started appearing in science fiction. The forest moon of Endor from

Star Wars is the most famous case with the more recent Pandora from *Avatar* coming in second. Both moons teamed with life, offering an entertaining contrast to our lifeless Moon.

An earlier example of a science-fiction moon is notable for its nonexistence. The enduring success of *Star Trek* made the planet Vulcan the quintessential alien world. A devoted fan base has since speculated on microscopic details of the show, including an inconsistency concerning the Vulcan moon. It is clearly stated in an early episode that Vulcan has no moon, but when *Star Trek* was reintroduced as feature films, two supposed moons are frequently seen in the Vulcan sky. Later publications have addressed the matter by giving Vulcan a twin planet, T'Khut (The Watcher), with a moon of its own, T'Rukhemai (Eye of the Watcher).

The confusing state of Vulcan's moons is both a symptom of changing production values and how the portrayal of alien worlds has evolved. Fictional planets need something to easily distinguish them from our world while still being relatable. Ideally, it should be exotic but achievable with a limited budget. One simple solution is changing the sky, which typically means a different number of moons. In script form, it's easy to state in dialog that Vulcan has no moon. It sets a memorable difference between Earth and Vulcan, but in films an empty sky looks incomplete. Alien exterior shots are more interesting with multiple moons. Such an idea had already been used on other worlds from the original *Star Trek* series. Multi-mooned skies have since become the standard trope of alien vistas.

Depicted as a harsh desert world with thin air, Vulcan bears a striking similarity to Mars except for being hot while Mars is freezing cold. The association is no mere coincidence as Mars was meant to be the home of Spock in early drafts of the series. Vulcans originally were known as Vulcanians, a reference to the Roman god Vulcan who has often been associated with Mars. The change likely was inspired by the ongoing definition of an alien world. Mars had been a perennial favorite for over half a century, but the promise of space exploration made the solar system seem too small. As the show solidified, Vulcan became an unfamiliar planet orbiting a far distant star.

As probes started orbiting and landing on Mars in the seventies, it shifted out of pop culture to become the dominant headline maker in real planetary science. Vulcan, and later Tatooine, would claim the title of favorite sci-fi home world, each borrowing the dusty arid landscapes of Mars. Tatooine has three moons—Ghomrassen, Guermessa, and Chenini—but their existence is merely as a set decoration for an alien world theme. Whether compared to fictional or real worlds, Earth's single moon is the exception and not the rule. Our overfamiliarity with the Moon causes us to underestimate its uniqueness. In an artistic effort to paint fantastic skies with a dotted array of moons, we are overlooking the Moon's purpose of making Earth a habitable world. Alien skies without a Moon such as our own likely will have no one to watch them.

Panic and Dread

The two moons of Mars are unique in that they are first mentioned in literature long before they were in fact discovered. In *Gulliver's Travels*, published in 1726 by Jonathan Swift, the two moons of Mars are mentioned as being discovered by astronomers from the fictional floating island of Laputa. This stunning prediction is not so amazing as it sounds when a few additional facts are considered. Shortly after Galileo discovered the first four moons of Jupiter in 1609, it was speculated that Mars would likely have moons as well, and if Earth had one moon and Jupiter had four, then Mars predictably would have two. In fact, Johannes Kepler mistakenly thought that Galileo had discovered them when he incorrectly decoded a secret message from him in 1610 that said Hello furious twins, sons of Mars. Despite the number being based on mere speculation, astronomer Asaph Hall discovered two Martian moons in 1877. He appropriately named them Phobos and Deimos. Translated from ancient Greek as "panic" and "dread," they are twin sons of Ares, the Roman god of war.

It took a long time to find Martian moons because they were much smaller than anyone expected, making their discovery even more remarkable. Although Mars is one of our closest planetary neighbors, it would be the last planet to have any of its moons discovered. Even Triton, which orbits the far distant Neptune, was discovered 31 years earlier. By the time Phobos and Deimos were found, there were over 20 known moons besides Earth's, including eight around Saturn alone. Finding the tiny moons of Mars required the massive 26-inch refracting telescope of the United States Naval Observatory, the largest of its kind. Even then, Asaph Hall almost gave up and credited his wife, Angeline Stickney, with the encouragement to continue the search. A massive crater on Phobos would be named in her honor for the small part she played in the big discovery. Even now, with almost 200 known moons in the solar system, Phobos and Deimos remain some of the smallest moons ever found.

The Martian moons are more like asteroids than what might be considered a typical moon. Phobos is only 22 kilometers in diameter, and its Stickney Crater is 9 kilometers wide, leaving an enormous gaping hole on its side. Deimos, at 12 kilometers wide, is even smaller and is approximately the same size as Halley's Comet. They are both so small that they aren't even well-rounded shapes, as they fall well below the limit where their own gravity would shape them into regular spheres. That limit of about 200 to 300 kilometers is sometimes called the potato radius because objects below that limit often have the irregular look of a potato. Their distinctly small size and irregular shape led early 20th-century astronomers to speculate that they must have been captured asteroids. This has been the prevalent theory until recently, when spectral surface analysis suggested that Phobos and Deimos are made up from material similar to the surface of Mars and are possibly remnants of a large asteroid impact. If true, this similar origin might be one of the few significant things they share in common with Earth's Moon.

Beyond size, the fundamental difference between the moons of Mars and Earth is the influence they have on their respective planets. While the Moon's influence on Earth and life is considerable and well known, Phobos and Deimos have essentially no effect on Mars. Based on what we've learned about Earth and Mars, this might be a critical difference in the development of each world. That is, the Moon played a main supporting role in Earth's stability that wasn't matched by Phobos and Deimos. Mars still has a weak magnetic field that helps it maintain an extremely thin atmosphere, but research has shown that long ago, Mars was different. Mars was once volcanic with a stronger magnetic field and a denser atmosphere. It might have possessed a core dynamo mechanism like Earth's but lacked the gravitational force of a large moon to help maintain it.

There has been repeated evidence of water found on Mars. There's every reason to conclude scientifically that early conditions on Mars were at least similar to that of Earth, with the added possibility that life could have once existed on Mars in very simple forms. One day in the future, we may colonize Mars and bring new life to the planet. Whether it will be the first life on Mars or just a restart is still not known. As research on Mars continues, we are observing the aftermath of what happens to a planet that was once like Earth but didn't have a moon like ours. Learning the failed history of Mars can give us an even better appreciation for the Moon's role in Earth's development.

Last on the Moon

By the mid-1960s, the winning balance of the Space Race had tipped in favor of the United States. The Gemini program was outstripping the Soviet Union's Voskhod, or Sunrise program, for publicity and technical milestones. Setbacks in the development of their N-1 rocket effectively ended the possibility of the Soviets going to the Moon.

The change in space flight goals affected other Soviet space programs as well. The unmanned Luna program would now become the primary means of competing with the United States for Moon-related headlines. American-manned Moon landings would be matched with Russian robotics, and this strategy was extended to include the unused Soviet Lunokhods, or lunar rovers.

Originally designed to be used by cosmonauts on the Moon to extend their range, they were quickly adapted to be controlled directly from Earth. The first effort at using a Lunokhod to steal headlines from the United States failed during a launch explosion in February 1969, but the following attempt, known as Lunokhod 1, successfully landed on the Moon as part of Luna 17. Beating the first manned lunar rover of Apollo 15 by six months, it was the first vehicle to drive on another world and remained in operation for 321 days, traversing 10.54 kilometers.

The achievement of Lunokhod 1 was significant but only a symbolic victory. It could not compete with the dominance of the Apollo program. A final point in the space race's legacy, however, can still be awarded to the Soviets. Their second and last lunar rover landed on the Moon on January 15, 1973, a month after Apollo's concluding mission had left. Totally alone on the Moon, Lunokhod 2 dutifully conducted its scientific mission for four months until it accidentally grazed a crater wall on May 9. Dust from the crater clogged some of Lunokhod 2's radiators, causing it to overheat and fail to respond to commands two days later. This marked an abrupt end to the now forgotten Lunokhods. Although disappointingly short-lived, Lunokhod 2 still set a new off-world distance record by traveling 42 kilometers on the Moon, surpassing the mark previously held by the lunar rover of Apollo 17. It was a final highlight for the Soviet Union's effort during the Space Race as the final three Luna missions yielded nothing remarkable. The distance record of Lunokhod 2 would stand for over 40 years until the Martian rover Opportunity surpassed it.

The short-lived triumph of the Lunokhods was lost among the glamour of the Apollo missions. Looking somewhat ungainly, like chrome bathtubs with lids on wheels, they still played a pivotal part in early space exploration. They proved that remote-controlled rovers were practical and a cheaper option to manned flights. This has since become a key component of all exploration of the solar system. Together, the two rovers returned over 100,000 low-resolution images, nearly 300 panoramic images, and dozens of soil analyses. In the true spirit of that era, they were robotic pioneers as their legacy continued in the exploration of Mars. They later would serve as prototypes for the Mars rovers Spirit and Opportunity, whose basic designs are remarkably similar. They were each powered by batteries that were recharged by solar cells and could be sent into hibernation to conserve power during the cold of night. Humans back on Earth guided them based on visual feedback from their cameras.

The final positions of the Lunokhods, or Moonwalkers, have been approximated to the nearest meter, thanks in part to the Lunar Reconnaissance Orbiter, or LRO. Many kilometers away from their starting points, their tracks can clearly be seen in high-resolution images. Until recently, they were the only two things that traveled on the Moon without direct human assistance. Their total time exploring the surface of the Moon amounted to 14 months, dwarfing the cumulative time of 80 hours spent by all the astronauts that walked on the surface. Mostly unsung to all except fans of Soviet lunar tech of the seventies, they still prove useful to scientists. Each rover had a retro reflector installed as part of its scientific package, and even today they can bounce back surprisingly strong signals. Their mission continues.

Robots of Mars

H umanity's first and perhaps only encounter with Martians occurred on October 30, 1938, at Grovers Mill in New Jersey. On that day, Earth was invaded during a fictitious radio news broadcast, and widespread fear and panic ensued. The adaptation of H. G. Wells' *War of the Worlds* was produced in such a realistic docudrama style that many listeners were convinced it was real. That the invasion came from Mars and not the Moon reveals the sensibilities of the time. *War of the Worlds* was published just a few years before H. G. Wells' equally famous novel *The First Men in the Moon*, but scientists had long discounted the likelihood of life on the Moon. Lacking compelling evidence, the science-fiction community had moved on to Mars.

Within 100 years, humanity would turn the tables on any future Martians by invading their world first. With the Moon abandoned in the post-Apollo years, and landings on Venus and Mercury virtually impossible, Mars became the next target for exploration. A new stage in the conquest of Mars began on January 4, 2004, when NASA's exploration rover Spirit landed safely near Gusev crater. Spirit was joined by its twin rover, Opportunity, just a few weeks later. Together, they began conducting detailed geological surveys of Mars with the goal of looking for signs of water and possibly life. Other probes had orbited and landed on Mars before, but this was the first time humans explored Mars remotely.

The rovers had been designed specifically for surface work that was projected to last only 90 days. After that, high amounts of atmospheric dust were expected to cover their solar panels, making them inoperable. Regular dust storms kept the panels mostly clear and their batteries charged. Spirit eventually would fail after six years, but Opportunity persevered long enough to be joined by a third rover, Curiosity. Together they have maintained a continuous human presence in another world for decades. This unexpectedly long visit allowed NASA to expand its goals, which included occasionally pointing the rover cameras upward as the Martian moons passed overhead.

During their extended stay on Mars, the rovers could conduct experiments to reconstruct an amazing geological history of the planet. Repeatedly, the Martian rovers found evidence that Mars once had water in abundance and was once a potentially habitable world. It had lakes, rivers, and a large shallow ocean that covered the northern hemisphere for millions of years. This dramatic discovery completely changed our concept of Mars. Four billion years in the past, it would have looked more Earth-like than Earth.

When the earliest life began on Earth during the Archean Eon, Mars was moving in the opposite direction, with its Hesperian era giving way to the beginning of a dying planet. The complete picture of Mars' demise is still not fully understood. Perhaps a weaker volcanism or a lack of tectonic activity caused its magnetic field to weaken. Without a protective magnetic shield, Mars lost most of its atmosphere and water to outer space.

Today Mars is a dead planet with landscapes looking eerily like dry climates on Earth. Even though it's colder, drier, and has less gravity, Mars is still much like Earth. Under different circumstances the Martian rovers might have landed on a world very similar to Earth. A day on Mars is only 40 minutes longer than on Earth. In fact, a Martian day is closer to a day on Earth than any other planet. We may yet colonize it, but our conquest of Mars comes too late to enjoy it as a habitable world. For now, we must settle on using robotic wheels to navigate the Martian terrain and robotic eyes to see everything from its surface to its skies.

Finding the Martian moons in the sky was never a central part of the rover missions, but making observations from Mars' surface became extremely useful in refining orbital data. With gravitational influences from Mars, Jupiter, and even each other, the moons' orbits are more erratic than originally suspected. When Demios was first spotted by the rovers, it was 25 miles from where it was expected to be. Martian-based astronomical observations helped pin down tighter orbits. This now makes Phobos and Deimos part of a special club, along with the Moon, as moons that have been seen from the surface of their respective worlds. It likely will be a very exclusive club for a long time, as there are no more rocky planets with moons in the solar system, with maybe the exception of Pluto.

Curiosity, the replacement Martian rover, has seen both Earth and the Moon from the surface of Mars. Seeing the Martian moons from Earth is not that easy and requires a powerful telescope. The difference in size is a further reminder of the Moon's influence on our world. Even if Mars had formed similarly to Earth, its tiny moons contribute nothing to its stability. Our massive Moon is a remnant of Earth's formation. Earth's unique volcanism and tectonic plates are a part of that formation and are therefore indirectly connected to the Moon. The forces that created Phobos and Deimos did not give Mars the stable dynamo to help Mars generate a magnetic field. As the moons of Mars circled above with no tidal influence, Mars slowly dried up to become the desert alien world we know.

To date, no evidence of life has been found on Mars. If it is ever found, it likely will be microbial. The lifeless Moon encouraged our expectations of a Martian civilization, but the lack of a Martian moon such as ours also determined what we may eventually find.

.

Fictional Worlds

I n a galaxy "far, far away,", the double sunset of Tatooine inspires us with a cinematic tease of an alien sunset. This iconic shot has now become our common expectation of what an alien sky looks like, and it is not likely to be replaced anytime soon. Landing on some of the larger moons of Jupiter and Saturn would provide us with a unique vista, but the only other planet we are likely to stand on is Mars. Our dry icy neighbor cannot provide us with a vista as grand as Luke Skywalker's, although it would certainly qualify as alien. The sunset would be familiar in that the Sun would appear a similar size and set at a similar speed. The more obvious difference would be the color of the sunset. During the day, Martian skies appear butterscotch due to heavy amounts of dust in the atmosphere, but at sunset there would be a striking reversal of colors. The dust triggers an effect known as Rayleigh scattering, resulting in blue evening skies that are like Earth in the daytime.

After sunset, the same Martian dust dims the hope of viewing a brilliant night sky, and the double moons of Mars do little to brighten up the night. Phobos has the lowest albedo of any known object in the solar system. It is the dullest and least reflective moon there is. Deimos is even smaller and appears no better than a slightly oversized dim star. Although not striking, watching the moons of Mars still would be a unique experience. At only 3,700 miles away, Phobos orbits Mars closer and faster than any other known moon. With an orbital period of less than eight hours, Phobos orbits Mars more than three times in a single Martian day, appearing to race through the sky in the opposite direction to Deimos. This frantic speed is not shared with its twin moon, which takes two and a half days to travel the same distance. The two moons regularly cross paths with each other and the Sun, but neither moon is large enough to cover the sun, and a viewer would have to settle for what is known as a transit instead of a full eclipse.

Mars has a long track record of falling short of our glamourous "alien" expectations. In 1877, Italian astronomer Giovanni Schiaparelli reported he had discovered a network of straight lines on the surface of Mars. He described them with the Italian word canale, a general term for "channels" or "grooves," but the inaccurate translation encouraged an incorrect line of reasoning. American astronomer Percival Lowell published several books supporting his theory that the canals were the work of an alien civilization.

Vulcan has a similarly disappointing history. Before its famous *Star Trek* connection, Vulcan was the name for a hypothetical planet thought to orbit close to the Sun. Its existence was predicted in 1843 by French mathematician and astronomer Urbain Le Verrier, who correctly had predicted the existence of Neptune. Le Verrier was so certain he was right that he named it, and it was even added to solar system maps of the era. Le Verrier and others searched for years in vain but never found it.

As Vulcan and Mars respectively became the predominantly fictional and real alien worlds, little attention was spent on their moons. This seems truly ironic as the importance of the Moon to life becomes more apparent. Our cinematic impression of the Moon is limited to its ethereal beauty. Multi-moon skies are a variation on a theme that became a trend for the sake of drama. The stoic consistency of our single Moon causes us to dream about worlds that are boldly different from our own, but we lose sight of the Moon's unique grandeur. The beauty of the Moon goes beyond what we can see.

Future colonists on Mars may one day watch the moons of Mars. It likely will be a lonely experience as there won't be any Martians or Vulcans to share it. If Mars had one large stable moon, it might have had a better chance at sustaining a stable environment conducive to life. At least there would have been a possibility, but it is certain that if Earth had moons like Mars, life never would have developed to eventually see those two alien moons. Multiple moons may make fictional worlds visually compelling, but when it comes to supporting life, one moon may be the only number that works.

Moon Secret 11: The Moon's South Pole is forever dark and colder than Earth's South Pole.

The South Pole of the Moon is located within Shackleton Crater. It's named in honor of Ernest Shackleton, an early 20th-century explorer who attempted to reach the South Pole several times but never succeeded. While parts of its upper rim remain in constant sunlight, the center of the 4.2-kilometer crater hasn't seen sunlight in at least 2 billion years. Thermal scans have estimated an approximate temperature as low as -185 degrees Celsius. That's over 100 degrees colder than the coldest known day at Earth's South Pole.

A Solar Eclipse

In that great journey of the stars through space
About the mighty, all-directing Sun,
The pallid, faithful Moon, has been the one
Companion of the Earth. Her tender face

ELLA WHEELER WILCOX

OCTOBER:
Beyond the Moon

Hunter's Moon (American Indian)

(How the Moon shapes our chances of finding alien life)

The Symbol of Intelligence

I t is said that Albert Einstein once turned to his colleague Abraham Pais and asked if he believed the Moon only existed when he looked at it. This story has since been paraphrased with Einstein being attributed as saying:

> "I like to think the Moon is there even if I am not looking at it."

This was Einstein's way of pointing out the absurdity of the new science that, ironically, he had helped create. He had paved the way with innovative brilliance early in his career, but beginning in the 1920s, he encountered a problem\he couldn't solve. At least he couldn't solve it to his personal satisfaction. Einstein's problem was quantum physics and some of its more nebulous conclusions about reality at a subatomic level. Werner Heisenberg, who became famous for his Uncertainty Principle in 1917, best sums up the apparent weirdness of quantum physics. The fundamental components of reality were not only immeasurable, but they didn't exist until they were measured:

> "The atoms or elementary particles themselves are not real; they form a world of potentialities or possibilities rather than one of things or facts."

For Einstein, this was too much. He had spent his career looking for certainty in the physical laws of the universe. Coincidentally, the Moon's existence had been crucial to Einstein for proving his general theory of relativity. Photos taken during a solar eclipse on May 29, 1919, revealed the Sun's gravity bending light by shifting the visible positions of nearby stars from where they were expected to be located. As a result, the Moon made Einstein the most celebrated scientist of the 20th century.

Einstein's issue with quantum physics has since been resolved. The Moon's existence was never in doubt. Today, it is commonly accepted that the rules of the quantum realm work differently than classic physics. Viewing the Moon is unnecessary to prove its existence, but perhaps the concept of its existence can apply to other uncertainties. The Moon has been essential to the development of our civilization and is extremely rare, and that combination may prove critical in determining the likelihood of extraterrestrial civilizations.

Mathematics is the foundation of our civilization's brilliance. We use it to predict and validate realities beyond our immediate senses. Einstein is best remembered for his sublimely simple $E = mc2$ equation, which describes the special theory of relativity. Both Einstein and the equation are cultural icons of human intelligence, but a lesser-known equation attempts to determine the likelihood of other intelligences within our galaxy. Developed by American astronomer Frank Drake, the equation is easier to understand than advanced physics but harder to solve.

Drake's equation begins with the reverse assumption that life could exist anywhere in the galaxy. It then asks a series of narrowing questions on the chances of another civilization rising to the level of interstellar radio communication. Each milestone of development would whittle down the probability of it repeating elsewhere in the galaxy, starting with the number of planets in the galaxy, then the likelihood of them supporting life, then intelligent life, and then finally a mastery over technology. Since the equation was born during the Cold War, an additional term was added to represent the possibility of a civilization destroying itself.

After some number crunching and best estimates, the first assessment of potential civilizations in the galaxy seemed highly promising. Starting with a pool of hundreds of billions of planets, Drake originally estimated the number of alien civilizations would be between 1,000 and 100,000,000. It has since been criticized as overly optimistic, but it bore out a conclusion that no matter how unlikely the chances of life are, the immense number of planets would beat the odds. The vastness of space made the discovery of extraterrestrial life inevitable. We simply had to look long enough.

The formalized search for extraterrestrial intelligence, or SETI, began in 1960 when Frank Drake started a four-month trial that involved scanning for radio signals around the star systems of Tau Ceti and Epsilon Eridani. These locations were selected based on a high likelihood of Sun-like stars in the area. No signals were detected during this time. The most notable event in the history of SETI occurred in 1977 at the Ohio State Radio Observatory project. Now known in popular science as the Wow! signal, it was discovered by astronomer Jerry Ehman while going through old data readouts. It was so amazingly strong that he wrote "Wow!" in his notes, and this later became its adopted nickname. Although the signal has defied a simple explanation, it was never detected again despite repeated attempts.

While the possibility of alien intelligence is intriguing, the likelihood remains an uncertainty. Beginning in 1992, the discovery of exoplanets was noted as a definitive breakthrough. A key component of the Drake equation could be reassessed with an optimistic appraisal. Probable new earths seemed to be common. Estimates that one in five Sun-like stars has an Earth-like planet might bring the total of Earth-like worlds within this galaxy into the billions.

As the search for exoplanets continues, the much harder feat of discovering exomoons may help resolve the question of alien life. The rarity of our Moon not only defines our civilization; it may define the probability of other intelligence in our galaxy. Somewhere beyond our Moon, there may exist an alien civilization like our own. It might have a similar understanding of mathematics and physics and even its own equivalent of an Einstein debating the certainty of quantum physics. The chances of another Einstein existing could depend on whether his home planet had a large moon of its own. We are asking the similar question to what Einstein once did but with a twist. Would he exist elsewhere if he had no moon to look at?

Life on the Moon

I n 1835, the possibility of extraterrestrial life erroneously was confirmed with a faked discovery of life on the Moon. What later became known as "The Great Moon Hoax" started in August with The Sun, a small New York newspaper, printing six articles on recent discoveries by British astronomer John Herschel. Supposedly intended as a satire, it was never announced as such and became wildly successful with reprints across America and Europe, which later included detailed illustrations. John Herschel's father, William Herschel, had famously discovered the planet Uranus among other great astronomical feats. He also had publicly asserted his belief in life on the Moon and was certain that evidence would one day be found. The articles were a long-awaited confirmation of William's beliefs. John Herschel was said to have been amused by the stories but eventually would be annoyed by repeatedly having to dismiss them.

The hoax might be considered the first Moon-related conspiracy. It was a sign of the times as scientific discoveries regularly were appearing in daily newspapers and becoming part of everyday life. Fictitious tales of life on the Moon were nothing new, but this was the first time it was reported as fact. The absurd story of life on the Moon reported with no proof was a humorous observation on the new fascination with science. It was also a critical commentary on the scientific speculation about alien life and the institutionalized religious stance that all life came from Earth. Excitement about life on the Moon faded, but Jules Verne would mention the hoax in *From the Earth to the Moon* some 40 years later. He also noted that a belief in alien civilizations was common among astronomers, even though under the scrutiny of science they had little evidence to back up their claims.

Contemplation of alien life is a natural extension of astronomy. It is said to be a lonely science, which comprises long nights of staring up at the stars with the full realization that they are like our own Sun. Surely the vastness of deep space would contain more life than one civilization. Even without proof, it was a perfectly reasonable idea. As the scale of the known universe continued to expand, it seemed more and more plausible. From there, it followed that not only did many alien civilizations exist, but at least some of them would be equal to or more advanced than our own. This idea has become a cornerstone of science fiction. The possibility that we are not alone in the galaxy has a romantic appeal. Based on the ideal of an overall intelligent benevolence throughout the universe, alien contact is a regular goal.

The appraisal of life on the Moon changed in the 20th century. Long before Apollo, astronomers had realized it had no atmosphere. No air meant extreme temperature changes and little chance of water. This effectively made the Moon inhabitable without artificial means. There was still a slight possibility of life on the Moon in the form of alien microbes. One microbe known as *Deinococcus radiodurans* has survived in orbit for a year. Perhaps some other species could survive in outer space indefinitely.

Accidental contamination by an alien microbe with disastrous consequences was the focus of Michael Crichton's 1969 novel *The Andromeda Strain*. Although the chances of such a scenario happening were slight, this was a genuine concern for NASA. The crew of Apollo 11 stayed in quarantine for 21 days after their return. In hindsight, this might not have been enough if there was a real danger. The microbes in The Andromeda Strain came from a crashed probe. The Apollo 11 command module splash-landed into the ocean and could have spread deadly microbes in much the same way.

Apollo 12 renewed the drama of alien contamination in 1970 when traces of microbes were mysteriously found on part of an old probe that it returned from the Moon. The landing site was purposefully chosen to be within walking distance of the Surveyor 3 probe, which had arrived on the Moon two years earlier. To study the effects of long-term lunar exposure, the crew disconnected and retrieved Surveyor's camera. When inspected back on Earth, scientists were surprised to find a few microbes living on the lens of the camera. The microbes were identified as a well-known Earth species that led to a staggering possibility. The bacteria had originally come from Earth and had not only survived the voyage to the Moon but an extra two years on the surface of the Moon. No other explanation seemed possible, and the sensational story made news headlines. It was later discovered to the embarrassment of NASA that its isolation procedures were lax, and the contamination came from the same scientists who were looking for the microbes. The only life on the Moon were the Apollo astronauts and the microbes that came back with them.

The Missing Civilizations

The Moon we see is always one second in the past. Light takes slightly more than a second (or one light-second) to cross the gap between Earth and the Moon. The outermost boundary of human experience just happens to be the shortest unit of time commonly associated with the speed of light. The Moon marks both a first step and the beginning of deeper drives in space travel, and our great effort seems tiny compared to the vastness of outer space.

Light takes eight and a third minutes to travel from the Sun, and this distance is also known as an astronomical unit. Mars, humanity's next proposed destination, is slightly over 1.5 astronomical units away. Such a trip will take nine months using conventional rocket technology, which is unlikely to improve soon. Beyond our solar system, the astronomical unit becomes impractical. The light-year becomes the standard measuring stick by default with most visible stars falling between tens to hundreds of thousands of light-years away. Our Milky Way galaxy is 105,700 light-years across.

The speed of light is a surprisingly old concept that was accidentally discovered while studying another moon hundreds of years ago. Not long after Galileo's discovery of Jupiter's first known moons, it was noted that Io moved fast enough to visibly change its position in a single night. This meant that Io could act as a natural clock for navigation at sea. This idea was abandoned when further observations revealed irregularities in its orbital frequency. Danish astronomer Ole Roemer concluded in 1676 that the change was due to the speed of light and a shift in the great distance between Jupiter and Earth. As Jupiter's relative position changed, light needed either less or more time to reach Earth. This resulted in slight variations when measuring Io's orbit. Roemer used this discrepancy to estimate that light would take 22 minutes to cross the diameter of Earth's orbit. Although inaccurate, Roemer's work was impressive for its time. Today, we know that it takes approximately 16.6 minutes to travel that same distance.

Light speed is the harsh reality of interstellar exploration as it trivializes current technology. Messages from Voyager 1, which recently left our solar system in 2012, take over 20 hours to reach Earth. It took over 35 years to enter interstellar space and is currently traveling at 38,000 mph. By comparison, the human speed record was set by Apollo 10 at 24,791 mph on its return flight from the Moon. While it monstrously eclipsed the Mach 1 sound barrier that had only been conquered 20 years earlier, it still took three days to get back from our nearest neighbor in space. NASA has broken the record many times since using unmanned probes, but it is a somber reminder of our limited ability to travel through interplanetary space. Our first step into space has disappointingly led to a plateau of technology. Without near light-speed velocities, human exploration of the solar system will be a monumental undertaking, and the far bigger task of exploring our home galaxy is a virtual impossibility.

Our modern sensibilities about alien life began during the same heady time as the space race. An optimistic public latched onto the idea as it watched humans live in space. It had been already theorized that there were millions of potential Earth-like planets in our galaxy, but evidence for intelligent life has remained elusive. This is a perplexing problem that astrobiologists cannot shake. The uncomfortable prospect of searching for extraterrestrial intelligence is validating the possibility that it simply doesn't exist. With millions of inhabitable worlds, our galaxy should have produced thousands of civilizations and been explored many times over. The evidence for alien civilizations should be relatively easy to spot. This is the essence of the Fermi Paradox. Italian physicist Enrico Fermi is credited for the problem by way of a story from his colleagues. During a lunch discussion in 1950 that included such topics as alien life and UFOs, Fermi reportedly exclaimed:

"Where are they?"

In a more formal definition, the paradox concludes that there is no gray area regarding life in the galaxy. There are only two possible extremes. It is either teeming with intelligent life or there is none out there whatsoever. Thus far, the lack of evidence for extraterrestrial life is the strongest argument against it.

There have been many attempts to explain the Fermi Paradox. Proposed explanations range from alien indifference to the inevitable tendency of all galactic civilizations to self-destruct. While they are all plausible reasons, each seems more likely to be an exception than a general rule. Another possibility is that most civilizations eventually conclude that the small chance for meaningful success is not worth their effort. Like us, there would be no reachable worlds within their lifespan, and they similarly wish to avoid any negative consequences of interstellar contact. This could certainly explain a general intergalactic disinterest in space exploration, but it is still likely not a good enough reason for all civilizations to give up. If only a tiny number still explored, we would know.

An alternative method for an alien civilization to explore the galaxy comes from using self-replicating robotic probes. Commonly referred to as Von Neumann probes, they would possess an artificial intelligence and be able to endure the long journey between the stars. Upon reaching a new star system, they would locate the materials to build a new generation of probes capable of continuing the journey. Using this strategy, a civilization could explore the entire galaxy in no more than 10 million years. This concept has been a familiar theme in science fiction and seems a plausible scenario. The technology to build such probes is within our grasp, and once again leads to a disappointing conclusion. If we can build Von Neumann probes, then any other potential civilization could have built them too.

Going to the Moon is often philosophically viewed as humanity's first step in exploring the rest of the galaxy. Our early success with the Moon encourages us to go farther, but the Moon also leaves us with an uneasy reality. If we can explore the galaxy, then it's likely been done before. Even limiting ourselves to interstellar communication does not free us from the uncomfortable conclusion of the Fermi Paradox. We may still hope for finding the lost civilizations, but the possibility of being alone is very real.

The Rare Moon Hypothesis

We cannot conclusively prove whether extraterrestrial life exists in our galaxy. We would have to investigate every corner of the galaxy to be certain. Like the unseen world of subatomic particles, we can only speculate on the probability and search for confirmation. This comparison is not fair to either science, as many issues in subatomic physics are now well understood while the transformation of alien world into a civilization still has many unknowns. The Drake equation was a first step to address the existence of extraterrestrial life at the dawn of manned space flight. Since that time, there has been an ongoing effort to refine the original estimates for each parameter of the equation. Alternate versions of the Drake equation already suggest that the likely number of civilizations in the galaxy might be as small as 100 or even possibly just one. That low number fits with the lack of evidence suggested by the Fermi Paradox. Either the chance of detecting an alien intelligence is extremely small, or we are simply alone.

One common observation of the Drake equation is that there must be something missing. The process from habitable planet to civilized world may require extra unknown steps. This has become known as the Great Filter hypothesis. First proposed by economist Robin Hanson in 1996, it breaks down the development of human life into nine steps and points out that at least one might be an extremely rare event and unlikely to be reproduced elsewhere. The concept of the Great Filter has since been extended to the ability of civilization to endure long enough to create technology and then not be destroyed by it. This represents current social concerns ranging from nuclear war to global warming.

Another chief concern with the Drake equation is a better estimate of Earth-like planets. Originally, it was reasonable to believe that solar systems around other stars would develop similarly to ours. It was also assumed that Earth-like planets would only need to be like Earth in a few ways to be considered potentially habitable. The most desired feature was an orbit within the Goldilocks Zone. This is the optimal orbital distance where surface temperatures would be neither too cold nor too hot for liquid water to exist.

While an abundance of liquid water clearly enhances the chances of a planet to support life, the Goldilocks Zone alone is an oversimplification on the criteria needed to create another Earth. Earth has many other unique properties, some of which may prove extremely difficult to reproduce. This was the focus of the Rare Earth hypothesis published in 2012 by Peter Ward and Donald E. Brown. Similar in concept to the Great Filter, it inspects the process needed to create a world suitable for the development of life.

The Rare Earth hypothesis begins by asserting that much of the galaxy is unsuitable for life and only as few as 9 percent of the stars in our galaxy are an appropriate match to our Sun. It then builds a new list of rare factors that make Earth special, but perhaps none are more unique than having a single large moon. In addition to a stable axial tilt for reliable seasons and tidal energy to help power the magnetic field, the theory adds the importance of a stable atmosphere, plate tectonics, and an ocean as critical factors for the long-term development of life. All of this can at least be partially attributed to the Moon. In their updated version of the Drake equation, the existence of a large Moon not only becomes an important limiting factor but is likely affecting several other factors as well.

Earth is indeed rare, but the Moon is most definitely rarer. It has been estimated that the probability of a collision with a planet the size of Theia might be as low as one in a trillion, and there are still other things to consider about the Theia event. The collision with Earth had to occur in exactly the right way to make a planetary ring capable of forming into a moon. It would also need to occur fairly early in the time frame of Earth, making the odds of it recurring in the galaxy much smaller. Without the Moon, Earth would have been a solitary large rock where life might have developed only to die off before it could evolve into something with the ability to survive long-term.

If the chances of life evolving throughout the galaxy are at least a trillion times less likely than originally believed, then Drake's original estimate must decrease accordingly. The most optimistic appraisal of the Drake equation gives us 100 million civilizations, but when that is divided by the probability of creating a moon similar to ours, the result is less than one. If we accept that advanced life first requires the creation of a moon, the extreme rarity of that event forces us to contemplate that we are the only life in our galaxy.

Perhaps life can evolve through various processes that don't require an Earth–Moon system like our own. The are many speculations. So-called eyeball planets, where one side of the planet mostly faces its sun, could support life around their equators. Super-earths, twice the size of Earth, would be able to maintain a strong magnetic field for a longer period than Earth without the need for a moon. Conveniently for astronomers, super-earths are also a lot easier to identify with current technology. It's also possible that planets could exist around red dwarf stars, which are smaller, longer-lived, and more common than the Sun. While all these scenarios encourage a continued search, Earth admittedly remains rare.

Among the excitement surrounding exoplanets, there is a sobering possibility that only one path from microbes to intelligent life requires a moon. If a moon is a crucial component in the development of life, the very reason for our unique existence could be right in front of us every night. There is no need to look beyond the Moon for extraterrestrials. The Moon may be proof that we are completely alone in the galaxy, but it is also a symbol of how special life can be. In a very real way, the Moon is our reason for existence, and we have been staring at it the whole time. We have peered past it while looking for a connection from deep space, but the answer to one of our deepest mysteries could be as close as it gets.

Moon Secret 12: The Moon has two different sides.

The familiar light and dark patterns on the surface of the Moon do not repeat on its far side. The maria or "oceans" appear almost exclusively on the near side. New research points to a devastating lunar impact 4.2 billion years ago as a likely cause. The scale of destruction can be seen in the size of the resulting crater. Appearing at the bottom of the Moon mostly on its far side, the South Pole-Aitken crater has a diameter of 1,600 miles (2,500 km) and is the largest-known lunar crater. Recent simulations of the impact reveal it also generated a massive plume of heat which traveled through the Moon's interior to chemically weaken its near side, making it more susceptible to volcanic eruptions.

The Moon

And if she faintly glimmers here,
And paled is her light,
Yet always in her proper sphere
She's mistress of the night.

HENRY DAVID THOREAU

NOVEMBER:
Children of the Moon

The Snow Moon (Medieval England)

(The secret origin of everything)

The Other Origin

The first person to suggest that Earth and the Moon had a common origin was George Darwin in 1884. He proposed that the Moon broke off from Earth at an early stage of development due to the centrifugal force of an extremely fast rotation. He even suggested that the wide and deep Pacific Ocean was the likely spot where the two celestial spheres had been connected. His basic assumption that they had once been a single object would eventually prove to be correct. Some equations from his theory are still useful, but the underlying reasoning was completely wrong.

George Darwin's personal origin has become more notable than his scientific work, as his last name suggests. His father, Charles Darwin, became famous for his groundbreaking contributions to the theory of evolution. His formative work, *On the Origin of Species*, first published in 1859, became the foundation of a science that maps the earliest history of life.

George Darwin's Moon theory never found strong support among other scientists. Most felt Earth would have needed to be spinning unreasonably fast for it to be true, and there was no evidence to indicate it ever had. The best argument in favor of his theory was that the Moon had a similar density to Earth's mantle, the layer of Earth just below the crust. However, this fact alone wasn't conclusive proof. Further evidence of a common origin wouldn't be found until after humans went to the Moon.

Variations on the Moon Fission theory had been around for a while, but it slowly lost its credibility during the early 20th century to be replaced with a more plausible Moon Capture theory. The Moon was instead thought to be a rogue object that traveled independently through the solar system until Earth's gravity captured it. This became the commonly accepted explanation of the Moon's origin until disproved by moon rocks returned by the Apollo astronauts.

While George Darwin was at least on the right track with his common origin theory, he is largely forgotten today compared to his father. However, it wasn't failure that led to George Darwin's lack of notoriety. Virtually all theories on the origin of the Moon have shared a similar fate. Even the current prevailing Great Impact theory remains relatively obscure compared to the concept of human evolution. You will find no iconic images of the Moon's beginnings on t-shirts, nor is there a concerted effort to have the subject banned from schools.

When Charles Darwin first published his work on evolution, the response was mixed and divisive. Some philosophers saw the concept of evolving from lower primates as humorous or distasteful, but there were at least some in the Church of England who viewed it as part of a greater plan. Interestingly, the question of human evolution was barely addressed by Darwin, but he had made a definitive argument for the general process of evolution. This quickly pulled Darwin into the center of the philosophical debate of the origin of humanity. When his son George published his theory on the Moon's origin 25 years later, it only received a fraction of the attention of his father's work and never went beyond the scientific community.

In November 1971, American paleoanthropologist Donald Johanson found two fossils in the Afar Triangle region of Ethiopia. When he put them together, they clearly formed a knee joint of an upright walking hominin. Humanity was still in the middle of their first stroll on the Moon as Apollo 15 had taken its turn just a few months earlier. Johanson returned to the site three years later to discover the famous Lucy, a 320-million-year-old humanoid that walked on two legs. Named after the 1967 Beatles' song *"Lucy in the Sky with Diamonds,"* she was the icon of progressive ideas from that era. Many concepts of evolution became mainstream during the sixties, with books such as *The Territorial*

Imperative and *The Naked Ape*. These would be the early focal points of human evolution until the science of genetics would offer an alternative hard proof.

Astronauts would bring back geological proof of the Moon's origin with a similar timetable. The Great Impact theory dates from the same year as the discovery of Lucy. The mechanics of genetics eventually would confirm Charles Darwin's theory of the evolutionary adaptation and the origin of species, but the origin of the Moon was confirmed even sooner. While evolution often triggered a fierce ideological debate, the Moon's origin largely was spared from wide-scale controversy. Unknown to most, the Moon gave us a way of seeing our origins from a different perspective.

A Broken Moon

U nder the peering eyes of a telescope, the Moon loses its luster and mystique. Covered with craters from a battering of meteors, the medieval tale of an old Man in the Moon seems a more befitting image than that of a youthful goddess of spring. For a time, this symbol might have been doubly appropriate as it was thought that the only eyewitness account of a visible lunar impact came from medieval times.

The remarkable account of the broken Moon is found in the chronicles of Gervase of Canterbury. On June 18, 1178, a group of five monks looked up at the crescent moon an hour after sunset and watched in amazement as its upper half split in two. A terrifying description follows the split:

> "[A] flaming torch sprang from the gap and spew fire, hot coals and sparks."

In 1976, geologist Jack B. Hartung theorized that the position of the strike from the story matched the location of a known crater called Giordano Bruno, one of the youngest craters of its size on the Moon. The resulting plume of ejected material seemed like a good match for the monks' cataclysmic description, and for a time it was considered a reasonable possibility.

As coincidence would have it, the crater is named after a medieval monk. Giordano Bruno was an Italian friar who championed the astronomy views of Copernicus and was later burned at the stake for heresy. He often is celebrated as a martyr who was unfairly punished for his scientific beliefs, but this might not be the case. Bruno's trial was due to his radical spiritual teachings, and the reason for his ultimate demise is still debated.

The impact theory behind his namesake crater has since been proven wrong. Such a massive lunar strike would have created a shower of debris that would have pummeled Earth for a solid week. There are no follow-up accounts from the monks or anywhere in the world that such a thing ever happened. It is far more likely that the monks saw a meteor striking Earth's atmosphere at their location instead. From their perspective, the impact occurred in front of the Moon and not on its surface.

With thousands of craters, it's easy to believe that the Moon has protected us from similar impacts, but this is also a myth. The Moon's gravity is almost 100 times weaker than Earth's and has virtually no effect on Earthbound asteroids. The Moon and Earth have a similar impact history as they travel together through the same part of the solar system. Previous strikes are easier to see on the Moon. With an absence of Earth's weather patterns to erode them, most craters on the Moon stand relatively unchanged even after millions of years. This makes the Moon an invaluable treasure trove for clues to Earth's earliest past.

By counting smaller craters in and around it, Giordano Bruno crater is now estimated to be four million years old. Before lunar samples were retrieved by Apollo, astronomers used similar techniques to estimate the Moon's age. While the Moon's craters remain intact, the impact rays that surround them gradually fade. This is due to exposure of the solar winds and micrometeorites, a process known as space weathering. Fainter impact rays belong to older impact sites, and simple comparisons of craters can determine a layered history. The Copernicus Crater is a good example of this technique as it lies close to a similar but much older crater with an impact pattern that has mostly disappeared.

Studies of the Moon's geology have led to more complete theories about the Moon's history. Evidence suggests that the Moon suffered a true cataclysm billions of years ago. This was first discovered in the moon rocks returned by Apollo 15, 16, and 17, and further confirmed with some lunar meteorites. Scientists found that many of these rocks contained impact melts that resulted from massive collisions. Radioactive dating of these impact melts indicated that the heavy bombardments occurred within a relatively small-time frame—between 3.8 and 4.1 billion years ago.

Impacts the size of the crater Giordano are a thing of the distant past. Current protection from meteors comes from Earth's atmosphere, which does an effective job. About 25 million smaller meteors collide with Earth every day, but almost all burn up in the atmosphere. Occasionally one is big enough to cause a dramatic explosion, and this is now suspected to be what the monks witnessed back in 1178.

The Moon protects us from many things. Its gravity provides us with stable seasons and a reinforced magnetic field. On a quiet summer evening in 1178, it protected five monks from being struck by an incoming meteor. While it offers no direct protection, the Moon sustains our atmosphere. Long before the monks thought they saw it break in two, and long before monks existed, the Moon had been protecting us from similar meteor strikes. Without the Moon, there would be no monks around to witness its beauty. We live under a protective shield, and most of us are unaware of the ongoing bombardments or the Moon's part in Earth's defense. The Moon protects us from the same force that produces its most notable features. Without the Moon, Earth's surface would look much the same as the weathered old Moon.

States of Life

The Moon is often thought to be the Sun's opposite. Similar in size from our viewpoint, but different in appearance, the two primary orbs rule over night and day and have been assigned a long list of virtues to govern: dark and light, cold and hot, female and male, love and wisdom, and beauty and strength, to name just a few. If they weren't the original basis for the origin of opposites, they certainly embodied the idea.

The unlikelihood of the Sun and Moon being so similar when viewed from Earth has been used as an argument for our reality being a digital simulation portrayed in films like *The Matrix*. The basis for the argument is the occurrence is so unlikely that it must be contrived. Speculation on the concept is beyond this book, but the coincidence itself can just as easily indicate the opposite. The near perfect fit of a solar eclipse is just a byproduct of the Moon's incredible rarity. If it theoretically looked any different than it did, life wouldn't be around to see it.

The real digital simulation of the 21st century is the computer-driven world of our own making. Numeric opposites are the hidden fabric of our daily lives. Every program, app, or data file is a series of zeros and ones that might represent anything. This amazing power of binary numbers was first noticed by 17th-century German mathematician Gottfried Leibniz with his discovery of the *I Ching*. The I Ching is an ancient Chinese book of divination containing 64 pages. Each page of the *I Ching* represents a different philosophical state of life and is referenced by a randomly generated symbol of solid and broken lines called a hexagram.

Leibniz was likely the first Western thinker to encounter the *I Ching*, and he recognized hexagrams as a form of binary numbers. Yin and yang were just a different representation of ones and zeros, and he saw the *I Ching* as a bridge between science and philosophy. Two hundred years after Leibniz, computer pioneer Ada Lovelace suggested using binary numbers as a programming language that allowed instructions to be stored digitally. Data storage on a modern computer is the same as the *I Ching*. The only difference is that a single byte of data comprises eight bits or lines of information instead of six. The states of life from the *I Ching* evolved to become program instructions.

Computers have continued their evolution to become an integral part of life, with one of the biggest steps happening on the way to the Moon. It has been estimated that the Apollo program accelerated computer technology by decades. Human and cybernetic worlds are now woven tightly together, and that merger began with a joint flight to the Moon. Although their processing power is now seen as primitive, Apollo's computers had many things in common with the ones we use today. The Saturn V had its own dedicated computer that ran system checks before liftoff. During launch, it sent adjustment signals to the individual engines at a rate of 25 times a second.

Once in space, the astronauts used the Apollo navigation and guidance computer on both the command and lunar modules, and its advanced design may have saved Apollo 11. Despite being accidentally overloaded with extra data, the computer could focus on the most important tasks while landing on the Moon. It was a prototype for the first wave of personal computer development that began in the late 1970s.

As the space race wound down, it had a brief extension into the world of chess. In 1972, American prodigy Bobby Fischer defeated Soviet Boris Spassky in a legendary match that provided another win for the United States in the Cold War PR column. Although they had been essential for getting us to the Moon, computers of that era were embarrassingly poor at chess, but our human competitive edge didn't last that long. The digital descendants of those computers now routinely beat the best human players. They may not have claimed world domination as once feared, but computers have become a dominant part of our lives.

Of all the benefits we have gained from the surge of digital technology that followed Apollo, perhaps the most profound is the ability to understand our own code. The emergence of genetic science has mirrored the development of computers as the same infrastructure has driven the two. The discovery of DNA in 1952 was quickly followed within a few years by the launch of Sputnik and the appearance of integrated circuits. Today the Human Genome Project, which is a complete mapping of all 3.2 billion base pairs of genetic information, is stored as computer data. The concept of DNA is now a common part of our lives. We use it to search for family origins, but DNA can take us further back in time. Within every cell of our body lies the original structures of life. We are our own best evidence for evolution.

Using the *I Ching* as a starting point, binary code can trace its origin to at least the ninth century B.C. By comparison, DNA code is a million times older, but there are some interesting similarities that make it easier to understand. The DNA molecule also encodes states of life, but these states are biological instead of philosophical. Hexagrams can be broken down into sets of three lines known as trigrams that represent fundamental forces of the universe. In DNA, solid and broken lines are replaced by letter pairs of A and G, or C and T, which are shorthand for four organic molecules known as nucleotides. Nucleotides can also be organized into groups of three lines called codons, such as AGA or GCA. In a pleasing correlation that Leibniz would have enjoyed, each codon forms one of the 20 amino acids that are the fundamental building blocks of all life.

The Moon's impact on our digital world is clear, but if we look to the distant past, we can find a similar nurturing effect for the natural world. The early theory on DNA's origin considered tidal pools as likely incubators. If correct, the Moon would have made its first direct influence on life during this time. Along the shores around a new earth, the rising and evaporating saline waters would break apart and reassemble proto-nucleic acid fragments, eventually emulating the process of duplication themselves. Another competitive theory favors deep sea thermal vents to that of tidal pools. In either case, tidal pools would have still acted as stable areas for amino acids and early forms of life.

Billions of years ago the Moon loomed larger in Earth's sky, causing tides ten times higher than today. Just like the post-Apollo technological explosion, the Moon's presence accelerated a similar explosion of biological life billions of years ago. Long before the I Ching and the concept of opposites existed, the Moon combined with the Sun to become primal forces of our world. The Sun provided the energy and warmth, and the Moon provided the gentle and predictable forces of change. Their interaction made the complexity of life possible, and we see the result in the intricate patterns of life all around us.

Dancing by Moonlight

Every spring during the light of a full moon, there is a mass spawning of coral all along the Great Barrier Reef off Australia's coast. The event doesn't occur precisely on a full moon, but it is thought that lunar illumination somehow triggers one of nature's best light shows. Within a few days of a full moon, dozens of coral species collectively release their eggs. It is unclear whether the timed release takes advantage of the extra light or if the light of the Moon is the signaling mechanism. Although it might not be fully understood, the lunation effect is a documented part of nature and is found in other animals as well. This often is used as an argument for a possible lunar effect in humans. While scientists have searched for such an effect, one has yet to be found. Humans have left that link to the Moon behind.

Except for a few insects, almost all lunar-influenced behaviors are limited to simple marine animals. This connection is to be expected as they are more dependent on tidal changes for a successful life. Tidal flow increases mobility, and a wider territory improves chances for finding food, mating, and exploration of new habitats. This ability is billions of years old and has been used since the earliest single-celled organisms. The Moon has been affecting life on Earth for as long as there has been life.

Two to three billion years ago, the Moon was much closer and would have appeared five to ten times bigger in the sky. It also was nearing the end of its volcanic phase and many of the lunar maria were filled with glowing lava. No animals or humans would have enjoyed such an amazing sight as eyes had not yet come into being, but the Moon was having a big impact on life. With the ocean tides up to 100 feet high and occurring every six hours, tidal pools covered vast sections of land.

These tidal pools would have been a perfect combination of organic material and relatively calm waters. They were perfect incubators and encouraged the development of a wide variety of microbial life. While the most likely location for early life to develop is still actively debated, tidal pools definitely played a major part in ongoing development and are still considered a likely home for the origin of DNA.

Over the course of the next billion years, life transformed from simple bacteria into the first multi-celled plants and animals, which would be followed by a massive diversification called the Cambrian explosion. During this time, the consistent Moon-driven tides acted as a reliable pump and kept the ocean temperatures relatively stable. We can see evidence of life interacting with the tides in marine fossils from that time. Just like they do today, nautiluses grow a new chamber in their shells every month, and ancient nautilus fossils from the Cambrian Era show us that a month only lasted 18 days. Marine biology has confirmed what astronomers and geologists already knew. The Moon was closer to Earth and moving a lot faster, and tidal actions were creating regular patterns in the environment to which life was clearly responding.

Today, there are only subtle reminders of life's connection to the Moon. Our biological ties have slowly diminished. For humans, they are all but gone with the notable exception of people who live and make their livelihood along the ocean coastlines. The daily routines of fishermen and sailors and even surfers are still driven by the Moon's tidal influence as they synchronize their schedules to the high and low tides. Our earliest links to the Moon are renewed by paying homage to the sea. This poignant fact was captured by President Kennedy in a speech to commemorate the start of the America's Cup sailing race in 1962. He delivered this speech only two days after he had called on the United States to "choose the Moon" as its destiny:

"It is an interesting biological fact that all of us have in our veins the exact same percentage of salt in our blood that exists in the ocean, and, therefore, we have salt in our blood, in our sweat, in our tears. We are tied to the ocean. And when we go back to the sea, whether it is to sail or to watch it, we are going back from whence we came."

We often think of Kennedy's inspiring speeches paving the way to a future with the Moon via space travel, but on this day, he reaffirmed a forgotten legacy. Within the oceans of the world, we find our original connection to the Moon.

PART 5:

ANOTHER WINTER
Returning to the Moon

Messages from the past provide guidance for our future. The Moon has much to tell us if we are listening.

December: A Message from the Moon

Moon Secret 13: There are over 1,600 named craters on the Moon.

Naming moon craters began in 1651 with the Italian astronomer Giovanni Battista Riccioli using names of prominent astronomers of the day. They included Copernicus, Galileo, and Kepler, even though Giovanni rejected the Copernican theory. This naming tradition has continued ever since, with most craters being named after famous astronomers, scientists, mathematicians, and explorers. While most of the night sky is named after ancient myths and legends, the Moon's surface has been named in honor of science. It's a monument to human achievement for all to see and share.

The Crescent Moon
Slipping softly through the sky
Little horned, happy moon,
Can you hear me up so high?
Will you come down soon?
AMY LOWELL

DECEMBER:
A Message from the Moon

The Blue Moon – A second full moon in a month

(Words of wisdom from far away)

Peace and Goodwill

What would the Moon say if it could speak to the world? A similar question was once given to the crew of Apollo 8 when they were put in the real situation of speaking from the Moon. NASA had told the crew that they would give a live speech during lunar orbit, which would be heard by more people than any other speech in history. As if being the first human beings to travel to the Moon wasn't hard enough, the details of the actual message were left up to the crew. The task proved to be too great.

The astronauts could come up with nothing. Needing help, Mission Commander Frank Borman reached out to his friend Si Bourgin who worked for the U.S. Information Agency. Bourgin similarly drew a blank and passed the problem on to Joe Laitin, a veteran reporter and public affairs officer who worked for President Johnson. Laitin also struggled to come up with something appropriate until an idea for the message finally came from his wife, Christine. The solution to one of the most celebrated messages of all time came from the wife of a friend of a friend.

By lucky coincidence, the crew was scheduled to arrive at the Moon on Christmas Eve, which presented a holiday connection. They would commemorate the success of the mission and the holiday season with a traditional Christmas reading from the Bible. Such readings were common on American television, but the crew of Apollo 8 would address a wider audience with a message of goodwill from the Old Testament, a section of the Bible accepted by three different religious faiths. On December 24, 1968, the crew took turns reading the first ten verses of Genesis, starting with:

In the beginning, God created the heaven and the earth.

When they had finished, Borman then closed with:

Good night, good luck, a Merry Christmas, and God bless
all of you—all of you on the good Earth.

Though the message was well received, it caused controversy. By selecting a message from the Bible that had nothing to do with Christmas, the implied link to the holiday wasn't as strong. By some interpretations, NASA and its astronauts had unfairly used the opportunity to expound personal religious beliefs. NASA was later sued on the grounds of separation of government and religion. The suit eventually was dismissed, but NASA became more cautious on how it handled both public speaking and religious matters.

Beyond the legal challenge, the predominant intention of the speech seemed to be one of self-reflection for the entire human race. Before the reading, the astronauts shared their own thoughts on the Moon as a vast, desolate, and lonely place. The astronauts were looking back at Earth and seeing a new view. It was spiritual in nature, but not limited to one religion. They could see the world as the Moon might, an amazing but fragile place surrounded by a void of darkness. For much of the world, this was a welcome conclusion to 1968. Protests over racial inequality and opposition to the Vietnam War had exploded into a series of violent riots, and the assassinations of Martin Luther King, Jr., and Robert Kennedy had mired the year in hopelessness. And yet far away from all the human chaos, Apollo 8 sent a comforting message of peace and goodwill.

Perhaps no one better than an astronaut could appreciate the delicate and precious nature of Earth and humanity. "In the Beginning" took on a new symbolic meaning, and the lunar missions were the beginning of a new global awareness. The first message from the Moon would be commemorated on a U.S. postage stamp, along with the image of Earth rising above the Moon's horizon. Many inspirational images from space would follow, including a high-detail photograph of Earth that has since become known as the Big Blue Marble. Taken by the crew of Apollo 17, it has become a symbol of a new age representing many movements for world peace, international humane efforts, and environmental protection.

While many positive changes followed Apollo, some efforts to improve life on Earth struggled. While nuclear proliferation treaties were signed, the arms race between the United States and the Soviet Union continued on into the 1980s. Pollution was finally recognized as a national and global problem, but global warming was relatively unexplored. The world's economy benefited from space race technologies, but still became heavily dependent on oil. As oil consumption grew, the United States could no longer produce enough to match its exploding economic needs. Newly found oil deposits in the Middle East drew power and attention to that area. The birthplace of the three religions unified by Apollo 8's holiday message of peace would become a violent and unstable place.

Nixon on the Moon

President Nixon's signature is permanently displayed on the Moon not once but twice, and no other human being shares that distinction. Appearing on both commemorative plaques for Apollo 11 and 17, the signatures pay an unusual tribute to a president who wasn't involved in going to the Moon at all.

By the time NASA accomplished Kennedy's goal, any remnant of his administration was gone. President Johnson had dutifully continued the work of his predecessor. In fact, it is arguable that he played a larger role in the space race than Kennedy. He had won the election of 1964 with a landslide victory, but in 1968 he withdrew from reelection. Without a strong, unifying candidate, Nixon won the election, and the fate of Apollo shifted into the hands of a political rival. Nixon saw the upcoming Moon landing as a perfect PR opportunity and actively sought ways to claim some of Apollo's prestige for himself.

All Apollo missions had similar plaques attached to the ladder of the lunar module. Honoring the mission and each member of the crew with their own signature was the original purpose of the plaques. In fact, a special replacement plaque had to be created for Apollo 13 because of a last-minute crew change. Because Apollo 11 had special significance, NASA had added a small speech to the plaque. During an approval phase, Nixon made some minor adjustments to the speech:

> *"Here men from the planet Earth first set foot upon the Moon July 1969 A.D. We came in peace for all mankind."*

The change was little more than the subtle addition of "A.D.," but it gave Nixon a presumed right to add his signature as the author of the quote. When he saw the final draft of the plaque with the crew signatures, he ordered his signature be added at the last minute. This resulted in extra complications for the ground crew on the night before the launch. Work platforms accessing the lunar module had to be left in place until the updated plaque arrived. This clever political ploy set the stage for future presidents to make their own mark on the history of space exploration. The Moon legacy has been incorporated into a brand of American greatness. While repeatedly successful in the short term, no other project has lived up to the prestige of Apollo, and Kennedy is still publicly recognized for its success.

The irony that Nixon had absolutely nothing to do with the success of the Apollo missions and therefore didn't deserve any official credit was pointed out by both the *New York Times* and the *Washington Post* at the time. The fact that he was being called out for stealing the show from two rival administrations didn't bother Nixon in the least. In fact, he enjoyed it. He had been Eisenhower's vice president for eight years but had narrowly lost the election to Kennedy. Now, he felt that his time had finally come. Nixon spoke to Neil Armstrong with a phone call from the Oval Office that was part of a live broadcast. It was a carefully orchestrated affair. Nixon's remarks were more like a small speech, and Armstrong simply thanked the president and briefly responded with an appreciative tone.

When Apollo 17 became the final Moon mission, Nixon used it as an excuse to add his signature again. There is extra irony in Nixon's name appearing on this second plaque because he all but assured it would be the last. As NASA's budget tightened in the early seventies under further scrutiny, Nixon did nothing to prevent the cancellation of later missions even though all the Saturn V rockets had been built. He even suggested cancelling Apollos 16 and 17 in April 1971 but was talked out of doing it. Any lasting reputation that Nixon hoped to achieve would be soon eclipsed by the looming Watergate scandal. By the time Apollo 17 returned to Earth, Nixon was facing the fallout of the Watergate break-in that had occurred earlier that year.

Nixon's name appears on the Moon a third time, although it might be hard to find as it's partially buried in the lunar soil. NASA had created a small memorial disc for Apollo 11 to deposit on the surface. The disc contained miniaturized messages of goodwill from 73 foreign governments with additional statements from Presidents Eisenhower, Kennedy, Johnson, and Nixon. Representing a diverse who's who of world politics, the goodwill list had some surprising inclusions. Romanian and Nicaraguan dictators Nicolae Ceaușescu and Anastasio Somoza Debayle appear alongside Indira Gandhi, the first female prime minister of India. Nixon hosted all three during separate White House visits. All three would later be assassinated.

Placing the disc on the Moon was one of the final actions of the Apollo 11 crew, but it was almost forgotten and simply tossed out at the last minute. Nixon was partially responsible for the disc's unceremonious end. His earlier phone call had crowded an already tight schedule, and the astronauts ran out of time. While they ascended the ladder that held Nixon's inspired commemorative plaque, Armstrong reminded Aldrin that he carried a bag of memorial items in his sleeve pocket, which included the disc. Aldrin hastily tossed the whole bag to the surface, and then Armstrong shifted it to the side with his boot.

In fairness, Nixon's administration did begin the transition of NASA into what we know today, but his name on the Moon is an empty symbol of fallen pride. A lesser-known but arguably more appropriate tribute can be found at the landing site of Apollo 15. A small statue known as the Fallen Astronaut lies in the lunar soil alongside a simple plaque listing 14 astronauts and cosmonauts who died during training. The names of genuine contributors to human space exploration appear on the Moon, symbolically joining the names of the astronauts that successfully completed the journey. Sadly, the list is missing the names of two cosmonauts and Robert Lawrence, Jr., who would have become the first African American in space. Even incomplete, the memorial stands as a touching reminder of sacrifice and a stark contrast to Nixon's long-forgotten signatures.

For all Humankind

s Neil Armstrong took his first step onto the surface of the Moon, he spoke the immortal words that defined the moment:

"That's one small step for a man, one giant leap for mankind."

While this was the intended quote, the "a" before "man" is indistinguishable on the recording. The mangled phrase even confused famed television news anchor Walter Cronkite when hearing it live. Armstrong initially insisted that he did say the "a," but later admitted that he might have "goofed." The question of what actually was said has never been settled, so the "a" has often appeared bracketed in quoted transcripts.

Much has been made of the possible lapse, but the answer seems trivial compared to Armstrong's symbolic intentions and how well they were received. NASA had solved the technical challenges of going to the Moon without addressing the social unrest that plagued the era. Armstrong stood on the Moon in good faith for all humanity, but there's a question whether he truly was representing all men and all women. This resulted in an often-reused quote from the time:

"If we can put a man on the Moon..."

This first half of the phrase was often paired with failed goals of social equality.

NASA's racial exclusion was part of a larger problem that America was just beginning to address. When President Eisenhower requested that NASA only use test pilots as candidates for astronauts, it severely limited who could qualify. Sadly, its notable accomplishments would be represented by one race and one gender in a time when there was a strong social call for the opposite. This triggered indifference among many African Americans who felt their cause was being marginalized at the colossal expense of Apollo. Soul-jazz poet Gil Scott-Heron expressed the mood with his poem " *Whitey on the Moon.*" It angrily repeats the title refrain after every other line until even the author has had enough.

Better racial and gender representation for NASA was on the horizon, but major milestones would have to wait until the eighties. Guion Bluford became the first African American in space as part of Astronaut Group 8. An opportunity to improve NASA's reputation was lost with the tragedy of Robert Lawrence, who has been called the first African American astronaut. Lawrence had an impressive military career in the sixties, rising to the rank of Major and obtaining a Ph.D. in physical chemistry. He worked as a test pilot investigating the gliding of unpowered vehicles, which later would contribute to the development of the space shuttle. In June 1967, he was selected for the Air Force's Manned Orbital Laboratory program but was unfortunately killed during an aircraft training accident in December of that same year. The MOL was later cancelled, and the astronauts of Lawrence's group were transferred to NASA's Astronaut Group 7, where he would have likely served out his career as a space shuttle pilot.

For women seeking opportunities in space, NASA proved even more challenging. An early attempt at astronaut gender equality was known informally as the Mercury 13. It was a privately funded program attempting to prove that women were qualified to fly into space. Many of the women tested exceedingly well and had more flight time experience than the Mercury astronauts, but NASA officials eventually would argue that their acceptance depended on jet fighter experience. This would temporarily close the door for women astronauts, as it wasn't a career option. The first woman jet fighter pilot, Jeannie Leavitt, wouldn't be born until 1967.

Women whose careers stayed on the ground fared only slightly better. At the launch of Apollo 11, JoAnn Morgan was the only woman in mission control's firing room. Even then, she had to be granted special permission. Gifted with an aptitude for math and science, she had consistently impressed her supervisors and had risen to a position of flight engineer. After a long career, Morgan remarked it had often been lonely. She could work an entire day without encountering another woman and was looking forward to no longer being the only woman in the room.

Even in entertainment, the drive for equality found new heroes. Nichelle Nichols had considered leaving her role as Lieutenant Uhura on *Star Trek* due to the part's limitations, but the character's visibility turned out to be an important milestone. Just as JoAnn Morgan was a sole female presence in mission control, Nichols was the only woman to appear regularly on the Enterprise bridge as well as the ship's only recurring African American. Martin Luther King, Jr., later brought home this point. She would credit the civil rights leader with talking her into staying. The decision would prove pivotal and have a lasting effect on efforts for equal representation at NASA. After *Star Trek*, Nichols became involved in a special recruitment project for the space agency. Many female astronauts would point to her as inspiration, including Mae Jemison, the first African American woman in space.

Gil Scott-Heron would also join the legendary pioneers of that age with his unique style of social commentary. His most famous poem, *The Revolution Will Not Be Televised* was released in 1971 during the middle of the Apollo missions. He is recognized today as a major influence on hip hop and rap music. His message from that time is equally as important as Armstrong's words. Humankind is striving to make those important first steps, but change is a process that begins with each of us.

Only a handful of lunar craters are named after women and even fewer represent men of color. Mirroring the similar imbalance found in the Apollo missions, it is a legacy of sexual and racial disparity in the fields of science and exploration. Since craters are typically named after famous astronomers, mathematicians, and explorers, there is a glaring lack of inclusion on the Moon.

In 2021, African American explorer Matthew Henson was finally honored with a named crater. He had accompanied explorer Robert Peary in repeated attempts to be first to reach the North Pole. It was originally thought that he got there slightly before Peary while scouting ahead during their famed 1909 expedition. Research now suggests the team fell short of their goal, but Peary was given sole credit for discovering the North Pole. A crater was named after him in 1964, over 50 years before Henson. That same year, the United States Congress passed the groundbreaking Civil Rights Act, and five years later Neil Armstrong made his famous all-inclusive speech from the surface of the Moon. We can accept a minor garbled flaw in those spoken words, but the promise of that message still needs to be regularly scrutinized.

The Silvery Gray Dot

I n October 1957, Sputnik 1 was launched by the Soviet Union and orbited around Earth for a couple of months. For a brief time, Earth had two satellites: The Moon, and a silver metal ball not quite two feet in diameter, whose name roughly translated as "travel companion." As we now know, the response to Sputnik's orbit triggered a series of events that ultimately took humankind to the Moon, but before the Moon became the final goal of the space race, it was seriously considered a possible test site for a nuclear bomb. Years before Kennedy's historic proposal, the Air Force had developed a secret plan known as Project A119, which would have detonated a nuclear device on the Moon's surface, intending to produce the largest visual impact possible as seen from Earth. The dust cloud would send a firm message to the world, especially the Soviets, of U.S. military superiority. The job of calculating the size of the potential debris field was given to astronomer Gerard Kuiper and his doctoral student, Carl Sagan.

Project A119 was eventually cancelled due to concerns over a negative public response. A manned Moon mission was a much more agreeable alternative. Sagan's unusually grim connection to the Moon remained classified, and its existence only became public after his death. Since he never could publicly comment on the work, we can only assume Sagan's feelings about being involved. While nuclear weapons in outer space are banned today, making the project seem wildly inappropriate, it would have offered a legitimate way to study the Moon's geology without the expense of a manned mission. Since Sagan was quite clear about technology and its moral obligations later in life, we might surmise that he justified the work as not an immediate threat to Earth or the human race, but as a rare benign use of nuclear weapons. It also seems likely that when he later spoke about the dangers of nuclear weapons, he was secretly acknowledging a darker chapter from his past.

Dubious as it was, Project A119 might be Sagan's most direct association with the Moon. He briefly researched the possibility of organic matter on the Moon in 1961 as a prelude to manned missions. He also consulted for NASA throughout the sixties, but mostly as an advisor to the astronauts. Sagan's real fame began after public interest in the Moon faded. By that time, the Moon had become a cold topic for scientific research, and priorities were consequently redirected to look beyond. Sagan's interests pivoted away from the Moon, although he continued to be involved in related areas of science. Apollo had been a renaissance for astronomical research and public interest in space-related topics, and both would shape Sagan's career.

Sagan became the director of the Laboratory for Planetary Studies at Cornell University, where he pioneered the study of other planets and how they compared to Earth. He was one of the first to note that greenhouse gases caused high temperatures on Venus and warned of a possible similar fate for Earth. With his continued ties to NASA, Sagan became a regular contributor to planetary space probes launched in the 1970s, first with Pioneer 10 and 11 and later with Voyager 1 and 2. He helped select the experiments that the probes would conduct and was a member of the team that interpreted the results. He also famously created a golden disc for each probe that carried a coded message about Earth and the human race. It could be said that Carl Sagan was the first to send an official interstellar greeting.

Sagan's fame would peak in 1980 with the launch of the highly successful *Cosmos* TV series and accompanying book of the same name. The success of *Cosmos* quickly propelled Sagan into celebrity status, and he regularly made guest television appearances. His passionate enthusiasm for the vastness of outer space was frequently mimicked with the misquoted catchphrase "billions and billions," but Sagan took it all in stride to make science more approachable. As scientific discoveries poured in from the planetary probes, Sagan was well positioned to share his insights with a wider audience, but he didn't limit his commentary to breakthroughs in science. As was often seen in the *Cosmos* series, he was a scholar of humanities and deeply concerned with improving the human condition.

As an astrobiologist, he was a huge proponent of the search for extra-terrestrial intelligence. He believed the processes for creating life might occur anywhere, and he had no reason to doubt that it wasn't the case. He felt that contact with an alien race would be all but inevitable, and making a first attempt was a worthy goal. It could unify the human species with a common purpose and elevate it to focus on global concerns. While he was optimistic about the chances of success, Sagan was adamant that the idea of alien life shouldn't be confused with that of UFO sightings, which he didn't see as credible. He pointed out that even in a galaxy teeming with life, interstellar travel would be relatively rare, and it wasn't likely that Earth would be singled out as a common destination. Earth was very isolated in the emptiness of space and far from alien assistance if we ever needed it.

In 1990, Sagan illustrated his point in a grand and poignant way when he requested that Voyager 1 turn its camera around and take pictures of where it came from. The probe sent back 60 frames, three of which were combined to create the *Pale Blue Dot*. At this time, Voyager 1 already had passed the orbit of Neptune and was over six billion kilometers away, and all that could be seen of Earth filled a single pixel. The incredible idea that all human history could be condensed into a single dot was an astounding and compelling idea for Sagan. In 1994, during a lecture delivered at Cornell, he presented the pictures from Voyager 1 along with his own personal observations as an ode to planet Earth and everybody that lived on it. It concludes with:

"To me, it underscores our responsibility to deal more kindly and compassionately with one another and to pre-serve and cherish that pale blue dot, the only home we've ever known."

Sagan would expand the Pale Blue Dot into a book that sadly became one of his final projects. Along with Cosmos, it represented Sagan at his best as he used science to encourage the public to see the world with a bigger perspective. Without mentioning them specifically, he was addressing the need for more humane global efforts, anti-war and anti-nuclear weapons ideals, and pollution and global warming concerns. These were familiar themes first brought to light by pictures of Earth taken by the Apollo astronauts on their way to the Moon. Sagan's Pale Blue Dot was an updated version of the Big Blue Marble. His message for global benevolence was an extension of the Moon's new symbolic meaning.

Sagan's view of the Moon wasn't perhaps as significant as his vision for the universe. He didn't weigh in on the Moon as a critical precursor for life. As expected, astronauts had found no evidence of organic chemistry on the Moon, and science has overlooked its involvement in the development of life on Earth until recently. Sagan took greater inspiration from the stars instead. When Sagan was a young boy, he had an epiphany upon learning that the stars were suns from distant solar systems with potential planets like Earth. This eye-opening view would lead him to an enlightened opinion of humanity's place in the universe. During his Cosmos fame, he would often repeat the personal mantra that "we are star stuff." Built up from the atoms from other stars, we were the tiny part of the universe that could understand itself. We can still gain a sense of that uniquely scientific and yet transcendental insight by looking at the Moon as it is our closest and most obvious piece of the cosmos.

Since Sagan first introduced us to the Pale Blue Dot, interplanetary probes have continued to photograph Earth from great distances. Depending on the distance and angle, the Moon is often clearly seen alongside Earth as a slightly smaller gray dot. One such picture was created by the Cassini probe when it took a picture of Earth and the Moon from the underside of Saturn. This isolated pairing of two pale dots allows for Sagan's thoughtful words of wisdom to apply equally to the Moon. Like Earth, we can find new meaning in the Moon for its rarity in the vastness of outer space. With discoveries old and new, we repeatedly have found the Moon's unexpected significance to our fragile home. Earth is the cherished sanctuary that Sagan proclaimed because of the Moon's place right alongside it. Earth could not be the Pale Blue Dot without its silvery gray companion.

Conclusion: The Moon Illusion

The Moon presents us with many memorable views, but none is more spectacular than a full moon rising. Dramatically staged against a darkened eastern sky, it is the quintessential image of the Moon, universally familiar and repeatedly captured in photos and paintings. With a little help from artistic license or an extreme zoom lens, the Moon balloons to fill the night sky, and its brightness contrasts with distant silhouettes and muted skylines. This classic view of the Moon conveys everything we feel about it, from mystery to romance, but it also perpetuates one of our oldest misconceptions. The Moon seems curiously larger than normal when seen on the horizon. While this effect is hard to ignore, it is incorrect. The Moon's size doesn't really change that much.

The phenomenon is simply and aptly named the Moon Illusion, and because of our long history of watching the Moon, it is probably the oldest illusion of all time. Everyone who has ever watched the Moon rise has been fooled into thinking the same thing. Aristotle incorrectly suggested the effect was a physical distortion caused by Earth's atmosphere bending light from objects near the horizon. Astronomers going back just about as far as Aristotle quickly disproved this theory by measuring the size of the Moon throughout the night. They discovered no noticeable change in size regardless of position.

Aristotle's mistaken conclusion is still the most circulated explanation for the Moon Illusion. This is likely due to its intuitive appeal and the fact that there hasn't been a total agreement on an alternate cause. Like the enigmatic Moon, the Moon Illusion defies an easy explanation. One possible answer, known as apparent distance, suggests that we imagine the sky to be a flattened dome, and the Moon appears to be larger on the horizon because our brains think it is farther away. Recent brain imaging tests suggest a similar but more complex behavior. When a large object is seen on the horizon, it triggers heightened activity in two specific areas of the brain which make it feel both bigger and closer.

The simple answer to the Moon Illusion is nothing more than a trick of the mind. Like many optical illusions, the result is a hard-wired effect of our brains. The hidden beauty of the Moon Illusion is a truth about how we see the world. Its false sense of reality mirrors our struggle to see things the way they really are. The oversized Moon reminds us of a bigger picture that we all share but often fail to notice. This is a free lesson in wisdom from the Moon and the Apollo missions that took us there. We are the creators of our own illusions, but we possess the ability to see beyond them.

We can see the Moon as a symbol of sustainability in that our planet is an island in space that we must vigorously protect. We can see the Moon as a symbol of unity and as a great equalizer. It reminds us of our shared rarity and fragility. As seen from the Moon, we are all fundamentally the same, and the giant strides we took to get to the Moon should be matched with equally bold steps to improve everyone's lives back on Earth. These are noble goals, and they are just as important now as when they were first inspired during those early years of space exploration. Staring back at the Moon now can refresh our priorities and recharge our resolve to make our world a better place.

Walking on the Moon changed the way we see the universe. Sciences such as paleo-geology and genetic research were just in their infancy, but now because of the technology that has followed, they have grown to become fundamental parts of our collective understanding. The origins of Earth and life are no longer unexplained mysteries or challenged controversial theories, but scientific realities. We know the Moon. We have journeyed there, and in doing so, we have found a new way of seeing our world and ourselves. Our beliefs may remain, but the Moon now symbolizes a science so deeply embedded in our society that it is impossible to ignore.

Over billions of years our world has changed many times, but the last geologic era, epoch, and age are now. We are living in a world at its most stable, and we arrived at this point in Earth's history because of the Moon's benign influence. We live in a vast and complex ecosystem that we totally depend upon. The oceans are deep, and the atmosphere is thick, but it wasn't always that way, and the resources of the world are not as infinite as they may seem. The lifeless Moon reminds us that our world is unique, special, delicate, and can't be easily repaired or reset. We must live with the consequences of each global action, no matter how subtle the effect. A lack of understanding of the science behind our natural world does not invalidate the need to protect it, and we cannot dismiss any warnings out of convenience. The Moon can only do so much, and it calls upon us to do the rest.

The Moon is our jumping-off point to a deeper perspective. It invites us to think on bigger scales and find higher ideals. It is so much a part of what we've become that it's one of our best resources for self-reflection. From our first looks to our first steps, the Moon represents the growth of human awareness from what once was unknown to what is now understood. It is the history of our civilization in the broadest sense, and it tells us who we are, where we come from, and why we are here. We can find truth in the Moon while it simultaneously ensnares our minds with an illusion we can't deny. To understand the Moon is to understand ourselves. We might look for wisdom elsewhere in life, but we will never find a more beautiful lesson than when we seek the brightest light in the night sky.

Enjoy the view!

Made in United States
North Haven, CT
04 May 2023